A. Caroline Schmehl
119 Spring St.
Reading, Pa.

STUDIES IN

CHILD DEVELOPMENT

BOOKS BY ARNOLD GESELL

THE NORMAL CHILD AND PRIMARY EDUCATION (WITH B. C. GESELL)

EXCEPTIONAL CHILDREN AND PUBLIC SCHOOL POLICY

HANDICAPPED CHILDREN IN SCHOOL AND COURT

THE PRE-SCHOOL CHILD FROM THE STANDPOINT OF PUBLIC HYGIENE AND EDUCATION

THE RETARDED CHILD—HOW TO HELP HIM

THE MENTAL GROWTH OF THE PRE-SCHOOL CHILD

INFANCY AND HUMAN GROWTH

GUIDANCE OF MENTAL GROWTH IN INFANT AND CHILD

AN ATLAS OF INFANT BEHAVIOR [TWO VOLUMES, 3,200 ACTION PHOTO-GRAPHS]

INFANT BEHAVIOR—ITS GENESIS AND GROWTH (WITH THOMPSON)

THE PSYCHOLOGY OF EARLY GROWTH (WITH THOMPSON)

BIOGRAPHIES OF CHILD DEVELOPMENT

THE FIRST FIVE YEARS OF LIFE:—A GUIDE TO THE STUDY OF THE PRE-SCHOOL CHILD

WOLF CHILD AND HUMAN CHILD

TWINS T AND C FROM INFANCY TO ADOLESCENCE (WITH THOMPSON)

DEVELOPMENTAL DIAGNOSIS: CLINICAL METHODS AND PEDIATRIC AP-PLICATIONS (WITH AMATRUDA)

A GUIDE TO THE STUDY OF THE YALE FILMS OF CHILD DEVELOPMENT

THE EMBRYOLOGY OF BEHAVIOR

HOW A BABY GROWS

FEEDING BEHAVIOR OF INFANTS—A PEDIATRIC APPROACH TO THE MENTAL HYGIENE OF EARLY LIFE (WITH ILG)

INFANT AND CHILD IN THE CULTURE OF TODAY (WITH ILG)

THE CHILD FROM FIVE TO TEN (WITH ILG)

VISION: ITS DEVELOPMENT IN INFANT AND CHILD (WITH ILG AND BULLIS)

STUDIES IN
CHILD DEVELOPMENT

BY

ARNOLD GESELL, M.D.

*Director of the Clinic of Child Development
School of Medicine, Yale University*

HARPER & BROTHERS PUBLISHERS

New York and London

1948

H-X

Grateful acknowledgment is made to the following journals for permission to reprint some of the material in this book: *American Journal of Orthopsychiatry* for "The Conditioned Reflex and the Psychiatry of Infancy." Copyright, 1938, by the American Orthopsychiatric Association, Inc. *Clinics* for "The Differential Diagnosis of Mental Deficiency in Infancy." Published by J. B. Lippincott Company. Copyright, 1943, by Arnold Gesell. *Progressive Education* for "The Changing Status of the Preschool Child." *Psychological Monographs* for "Some Observations of Developmental Stability." Published by the American Psychological Association, Inc. *Science* for "A Biological Psychology" and "The Method of Co-Twin Control." *The Scientific Monthly* for "Charles Darwin and Child Development," Copyright, 1939, by the American Association for the Advancement of Science. And for "Early Evidences of Individuality," Copyright, 1937, by the American Association for the Advancement of Science.

To
The Staff
of the
Yale Clinic of Child Development

CONTENTS

❦

Introductory

PART ONE

Methods of Approach

PART TWO

Patterns of Growth

[vii]

PART THREE

Clinical and Social Applications

Preface

This volume is a collection of papers, prepared mostly on invitation for special occasions. The titles of the chapters, therefore, suggest a rather startling variety of subjects. But in reality these chapters all deal with a single unifying theme, namely, the characteristics and conditions of child development.

In America, the study of child development has had a double motivation—a scientific interest in growth as a biological process subject to natural laws; and a humanitarian interest in the physical and psychological needs of the growing child in home, school, and community. There is no necessary conflict between these two areas of interest. Human development cannot be divorced from the cultural setting in which it occurs.

The Yale Clinic of Child Development has functioned both as a research clinic and as a service clinic associated with a School of Medicine. A devoted, co-operative staff have made it possible to maintain a reciprocal balance between so-called basic research and applied research. Our systematic investigation has been concerned with charting the normal ontogenesis of behavior (at thirty-four progressive age levels from birth to ten years). Since development is in itself an integrating process and an integrative concept, it has been possible to study defects and deviations of maldevelopment by the same methods employed in the observation of normal behavior. In the course of years the Clinic has come into contact with an extraordinary variety of developmental manifestations—in the preschool child attending the Guidance Nursery; in the developmental supervision and survey of feeding behavior of well babies; in the study of visual functions of infants and school children; in the preadoption examination of foster children; and especially in the diagnostic and advisory service for atypical and handicapped infants and children.

In spite of the vast diversity of symptoms, normal and abnormal, presented by children from every walk of life, we have been increasingly impressed by the lawfulness of an underlying process of development. Development is, indeed, the one inclusive function which all children share.

The task of a science of child development is to elucidate the mechanisms and the cultural goals which govern that supreme function. I hope that the present volume will reflect at least the potentialities of such a science which now is only in its first beginnings. Our emphasis on the social and medical implications will be evident.

For typographical convenience, the illustrations for various chapters are assembled in an introductory section. Part One deals with Methods of Scientific Approach; Part Two with special studies of Patterns of Growth; Part Three concretely considers Clinical and Social Applications with special reference to the developmental diagnosis of defects and deviations and the supervision of normal child development.

It is said that man needs new moral techniques and greater self-knowledge to manage a technological civilization. How can we possibly arrive at either the techniques or the self-knowledge without a deepened understanding of the laws and the very mechanisms of child development?

The most constructive cultural force that can be released in the years which lie ahead is an intensified conservation of the development of infants and young children. This must be a socialized conservation, felt and effected by the people as well as by their political leaders. This would entail vast extensions of preparental and adult education, and a more nearly universal form of developmental supervision under medical and public-health auspices. The life sciences may well have a basic cultural function in a yet more technological era.

ARNOLD GESELL

Introductory

CHAPTER I

"The Miracle of Growth"*

The task of science is to make the world we live in more intelligible. This world is filled with knowable realities. At one extreme is the Atom; at another extreme is the Child. In the Miracle of Growth these two extremes meet.

There are two kinds of nuclei—the nucleus of the physical atom and the nucleus of the living cell. Each contains energies derived from the cosmos through ageless processes of evolution. An atom can be pictured as a tiny solar system, composed of a central nucleus surrounded by electrons. In comparison, the fertilized human egg cell is transcendently complex, for its organic nucleus initiates the most miraculous chain reaction known to science—a cycle of growth in which a minute globule of protoplasm becomes an embryo, the embryo a fetus, the fetus an infant, the infant a child, the child a youth, the youth an adult, and the adult a parent.

With parenthood, another cycle of growth is liberated. And so it comes to pass that children, mothers, fathers, preparents, and grandparents can all behold the miracles of growth.

The exhibit which has been prepared with such imagination for your great museum is impressive, because it portrays the pageant of child development in full perspective. The central figure properly is

* Address delivered at the inauguration of an exhibit portraying "The Miracle of Growth" at The Museum of Science and Industry, Chicago, August 6, 1947.

[3]

the mother, who bears the child. But we are reminded that the child as an individual is equally derived from the nuclear chromosomes of a father. The incontrovertible importance of sound inheritance is made clear to all who wish to ponder.

Science is probing deeper and deeper into the mechanisms of heredity which underlie both the bodily and the mental growth of the human infant. Biochemists are identifying the genetic substances in the nucleus and cytoplasm of the growing cell. They have even begun to picture the possible shapes of the individual genes which determine the basic events of the drama of growth. By latest report, the genes may be likened to a curious double comb with a long row of protein teeth on one side and a row of nucleotides on the other. Simply arrange the teeth of these combs in appropriate sizes and sequences, and they will play a developmental melody. In a suitable environment, as a push-button exhibit may indicate, there will come to life a brown-eyed or a blue-eyed baby who reaches out for a rattle at six months, stands on his feet at one year, talks at two, and cuts his sixth-year molar at six. You see, it is indeed a prodigious chain reaction which deserves every possible insight that science and wisdom can bestow.

Accordingly, the experimental embryologist has brought the problems of organic growth into the laboratory where he is systematically analyzing the mechanisms of development. With the aid of microscope, staining methods, and recording devices, he boldly explores the growth processes of tadpole, salamander, sea urchin. He manipulates the conditions of growth to determine the effect of surgical and environmental alterations. He modifies the temperature and the nutriment of the organism, or he bombards it with X-rays to ascertain the developmental forces at work. He transplants tissue from one part of the organism to another part, or even transfers tissue from one species to another— all for the purpose of probing more deeply into the concealed miracles of growth. He transplants a regenerating amphibian tail into the eye chamber of a frog larva and discovers that the potential tail transforms

[4]

into a crystalline lens, a man-made miracle, based however on natural law.

In a growing system the components are in a state of labile equilibrium. One component has the capacity to *induce*, probably by some bio-electric mechanism, a new shape or arrangement in another component. The latent energy of the genes issues into patterned forms.

The medical scientist is especially interested in the harmonies and disharmonies of growth—disharmonies like cancer, and developmental anomalies such as retrolental fibroplasia which may blind the eyes of a human infant too prematurely born. Not without reason, the investigation of the physiology of development has become a major occupation of the life sciences. This investigation embraces plant and animal, human and subhuman, normal and abnormal manifestations.

Do all these varied laboratory studies throw light on the nature and needs of child development? Indeed they do, because we may be sure that the profoundest laws of development are universal and apply alike to the growth of tissues, to the growth of organs, of functions, and of human behavior.

From the standpoint of development, body and mind are indivisible. The child comes by his mind as he comes by his body, through the organizing processes of growth. Consider, for example, the embryology of *eyes and hands and brain*. These three are inseparably interlinked, both somatically and psychologically.

As early as the fifth week after conception (the embryo is but 1/4 inch in length), the eyes emerge as optic cups, the hands as limb buds, the brain as rudimentary cerebral hemispheres. The growing cells multiply at an extraordinary rate. Cells invade the diminutive limb buds and cause them to elongate. The outer segment assumes the shape of a paddle. Five lobes appear on the edge of the paddle, which in another month transforms into a five-fingered hand. Muscles and tendons attach themselves to the skeleton of arm and hand. Nerve fibers penetrate the muscular tissue. Nerve endings ramify into the joints. End organs by the thousands establish themselves in the sensitive skin. Thus the hand

[5]

becomes a patterned structure, elaborately connected with the central nervous system, including the brain. Presently, some of the structures are ripe enough to react. Arms and fingers make their first spontaneous movements. About the third month of gestation the eyeballs move in their sockets beneath fused lids, the fingers flex, open and close. These are patterned movements, embryonic behavior patterns. The mind has begun to grow.

There are six hundred paired muscles with billions of contractile fibrils in the human fetus. The fibrils are supplied by multibillions of neuron fibrils. The growing mind is part and parcel of this vast network of living filaments. The mind grows because tissue grows. Neurons have prodigious powers of growth. They multiply at a rapid rate in the embryonic and fetal period when the foundations of behavior are laid. The 5-months-old fetus is already in possession of the final quota of twelve or more billions of nerve cells which make up the nervous system. These cells continue to grow and to organize throughout the cycle of growth.

One may think of the child's mind as a marvelous fabric—a growing, functional fabric. Functionally the mind consists of propensities and patterns of behavior. If you should ask whether a newborn baby has a mind, the baby might well answer, "Look at my behavior patterns and watch them grow."

Note how *eyes and hands and brain* co-ordinate during the first year of life. The newborn baby can breathe, can suckle, can sleep. In the early weeks his hands remain fisted most of the time, but presently he opens his eyes and begins his psychological conquest of the physical world. He seeks the light of the window. At the age of 2 months, his eyes follow a moving person. At 3 months, he can look at his own hand which now is opening. At 4 months he can pick up a tiny object with his eyes, but not yet with his hands. At 6 months he can pick it up on sight. His grasp at first is crude and pawlike, but at 10 months he extends his index finger and picks up a crumb on his highchair tray by a precise pincer prehension. This extension of the index finger is an important event in the story of growth. It represents a refinement and specialization of the child's action system.

At this age the New Haven infant, and I believe also the Chicago infant, is under an irrepressible compulsion to poke and to pry and to probe. He uses his index finger as though it were a tool. He uses it as an awl to thrust, as a lever to push. His prehension and manipulation are no longer pawlike. He has made a neurological advance toward adult levels of skill, and he is discovering the mysteries of container and contained, and of the third dimension. He continues to progress from one level of skill to another, not altogether because of specific training or instruction, but primarily because he is richly endowed with natural powers of growth, which bring eyes, hands, nerve cells into increasingly complex co-ordinations.

By the age of one year his brain has sufficiently matured so that he is capable of inhibiting his grasp and of exercising voluntary release. Give him a dozen cubes. He picks them up one by one and then drops them one by one to exercise this new-found power of release. He disposes the cubes in random array, but at 18 months he uses them as though they were building stones and erects a tower of three blocks. At 2 years he builds horizontally, arranging the blocks into a wall. At 3 years he can rearrange the three blocks to construct a bridge. This is a lawful sequence determined by the intrinsic growth of the relationships between eyes and hands and brain.

Similar sequences determine the later progressions of behavior. The 3-year-old can draw a circle; the 4-year-old a square. The 5-year-old uses eyes and hands to mold objects with clay. The 6-year-old can use a pencil or crayon as a tool, printing capital letters. Seven-year-old boys begin to use hammer and saw; girls color and cut out paper dolls. The 8-year-old draws action figures in good proportion, and puts perspective into his drawings. The 10-year-old can build complex structures with an erector set, and he uses handwriting as a tool with freedom and facility.

This sketchy summary of the eye-hand-brain relationships indicates that the progressions of child development are governed by a ground plan. Growth is a step-by-step miracle—a gradual and not a sudden apocalypse. Each step is made possible only by the step that preceded. First the blade, then the ear; after that the full corn in the ear. As with a plant, so with a child. His mind grows by natural stages. The eyes take the lead, the hands follow. The baby grasps with his palm before he grasps with his finger tips. He creeps before he walks, cries before he laughs, babbles before he talks, builds a tower before a wall, a wall before a bridge, draws a circle before a square, a square before a diamond. Such sequences are part of the order of Nature.

With the aid of motion-picture cameras, our Clinic has documented thousands of behavior patterns and pattern phases at thirty-four age levels from the period of fetal infancy through the first ten years of life. These voluminous records show that although no two individuals are exactly alike, all normal children tend to follow a general ground plan of growth which is characteristic of the species or of a cultural group. Every child, therefore, has a unique pattern of growth, but that pattern is a variant of a basic ground plan.

The ground plan is determined by the genes. Environmental factors support, inflect, and modify, but they do not generate the progressions of development. It can be said with scientific assurance that when the infant enters the world, he is already an individual with growth potentialities which are distinctively his own. He comes into his racial inheritance through processes of maturation governed by the genes. He comes into his social inheritance through processes of acculturation. These two processes operate and interact in close conjunction, but maturation is so fundamental that it cannot be transcended.

We have been studying a pair of duplicate twins over a period of twenty years. Beginning with infancy and with the help of the cinema, we have identified numerous similarities and differences which demonstrate the basic role of maturation, in shaping the individuality of behavior even in extremely similar twins. If you are reluctant to acknowledge the importance of genes, you may say, "This is all very well for such physical reactions as walking, stair climbing, block building, writing, drawing, and motor performance. But does it apply to emotions, to morals, to personality, and to the spiritual aspects of childhood?"

Our studies show that the higher psychical manifestations of child life also are profoundly subject to laws of development. The foundation and the framework of human personality are laid down in the first ten years of life by processes of growth which continue with new intensity throughout the teens.

Psychically, the child inherits nothing fully formed. Each and every part of his nature has to grow—his sense of self, his fears, his affections, and his curiosities, his feelings toward mother, father, playmates, sex, his judgments of good and bad, of ugly and beautiful, his respect for truth and property, his sense of humor, his ideas about life and death, crime, war, races, nature, and deity. All of his sentiments, concepts, and attitudes are products of growth and experience. They are patterned modes of behavior which are obedient to the same lawful sequences which determine the patterning of posture, locomotion, prehension, and the acts of skill mediated by eyes, hands, and brain.

The culture, through home and school, through religion, art, and recreation, leaves its imprint on the growing child. The culture directs and guides; it helps to organize his goals and his conduct, but always he must do his own growing. In his growth he passes through recurrent stages of transition, disequilibrium and recurrent equilibrium. He does not mount at one bound to the higher ethical levels. His development takes a spiral course. With each turn of the spiral, the level of his maturity rises. We can have faith in the constructive essence of growth.

We must not lose faith if at the age of 2½ years, the child grabs a toy from his playmate; if at 4 years he calls names and brags and boasts and tells tall tales; if at 6 years he suddenly becomes aggressive in word and action. We do all that we can to divert his behavior into desirable channels, but we must recognize the nature of his immaturity. He is not necessarily depraved if at 6 years he appropriates something which does not belong to him. At this time he has a weak sense of ownership, even with respect to his own property, and he may give away his best possessions. He is in a stage of transition where values are not yet established.

But at 7 and 8 years of age he rapidly develops a sense of fairness, of honesty. He begins to think in terms of right and wrong as well as of good and bad. At 10 years he becomes interested in social problems and develops an embryonic civic as well as personal conscience. He may even discuss problems of racial minorities, gangsters, crime, labor and management, black markets. It is a golden period for planting liberalizing ideas and attitudes.

All this is part of the miracle of growth. For the laws of growth apply to all aspects of the child's nature. The child grows as a unit throughout the entire cycle of development. He comes into the world with distinctive potentialities of growth which are part of his inalienable rights. Very naturally, he manifests a spirit of liberty which has its deepmost roots in the biological impulsion toward optimal growth.

Growth, therefore, becomes a philosophical concept when applied to the affairs of human culture. Just as the Darwinian concept of racial evolution transformed our outlook upon human institutions, so the new biological doctrines of growth have vast social implications—implications for child guidance, for mental diagnosis, for health supervision, for the conduct of education, and for the very arrangements of our ways of living. In the light of modern science, we cannot define a system of ethics or of mental hygiene without acknowledging the relativities of growth.

To understand children, we must understand their ways of growth. This is why we need a science of child development to interpret the more mysterious meanings of child behavior. This is why the clinical science of pediatrics is becoming more and more concerned with the diagnosis and the supervision of child development. American pediatrics is embarking on a program of developmental protection which will embrace all children in their early years. It is altogether fitting that the present exhibit of the physical, the dental, and the mental development of the child should have been prepared under the auspices of a department of pediatrics in a university school of medicine.

At the moment, the physical sciences—physics and chemistry—hold the stage. This is inevitable because the immediate fate of mankind depends upon how the explosive fruits of these sciences are used. But when peace is assured, the life sciences as well as the physical sciences will hold the stage, and both together will be constructively addressed to the betterment of human relationships, and to the preservation of family life.

After all, do we need to draw a sharp distinction between the physical, the biological sciences, or for that matter, between science and the humanities? All nature is unitary. I think it enhances the significance of the Exhibit on Child Development that it will be housed in a comprehensive Museum of Science and Industry, where the visitor can see the triumphs of engineering and the remarkable products of our technological age side by side with medical and biological exhibits which portray the nature of the creative, inventive man who, with eyes, hands, and brain, brought a civilization into being.

But this civilization will come to ruin if man cannot preserve his mental and spiritual health. We need a more profound knowledge of child development to teach us the limitations of the human nervous system under the impacts of a technological culture.

This knowledge will come not only from direct studies of infant and child, but from the converging contributions of all the natural and life sciences. As governments and communities become more responsible for the support of science, there should be an increasing focalization of research upon the child and upon the family which is the fundamental unit of our social structure. Already our citizens are becoming more science minded with respect to their human relationships and to the problems of child care and education. They doubt the efficacy of mere indoctrination and authoritarian discipline. Sensing the dignity and worth of individuality even in the infant, they sense likewise the growth mechanisms which determine the mind and morals of the child as he advances toward maturity.

Knowing something of the beauty and relentless precision of engines and machines, modern man is ready for new realistic insights into the mechanisms of development, mechanisms which are as exacting as the laws of gravitation. The task of science is to increase the intelligibility of the lawful factors which make man what he is, and what he might be. Such intelligibility leads to tolerance among grown men, and to humaneness between adult and child. With science and yet more science, the race may hope to attain higher orders of morality and subjugate the lingering wickedness which a million years of evolution have not abolished.

A science of man which recognizes the dignity of the individual infant, accordingly, could become a creative force in the atomic age. It would heighten and multiply human values. It would diffuse mutual understanding.

In a more sincerely sustained effort to understand children, men and women of maturity will better comprehend themselves and their fellows. Thus we might slowly acquire those moral techniques which are necessary for the control of a technological culture, and which also are necessary for an answer to the age-old prayer in which we ask to be delivered from evil.

To sum up in a sentence, we cannot conserve the mental health of children, we cannot make democracy a genuine folkway, unless we bring into the homes of the people a *developmental philosophy* of child care rooted in scientific research.

CHAPTER II

A Visual Chapter

Vision is the most avid of all our senses. For this reason we have museums, charts, photographs, microscopes, telescopes, television, and motion pictures. Visual hunger is virtually insatiable. One can never see enough. If it were possible we should like to see the miracle of growth in its innermost essence.

The embryologist with a microscope focused upon the transparent tail of a living frog tadpole has witnessed the growing tips of single nerve fibers groping their way with amoeboid movements. Cinemicrophotographs of the fast-motion type depict the advance of a growth cone spinning a nerve fiber behind it, the cone traveling as much as one-fifth of a millimeter in less than six hours. Such visual records give an intimation of the nature of organic growth. To see is to believe that growth is indeed a living process.

Aristotle in his fresh outlook upon the world caught the significance of vision: "All men by nature desire to know. An indication of this is the delight we take in our senses; for even apart from their usefulness they are loved for themselves; and above all others the sense of sight. For not only with a view to action, but when we are not going to do anything, we prefer seeing to everything else. The reason is that this, most of all senses, makes us know and brings to light many differences between things."

The study of Child Development, therefore, invites the use of visual methods which delineate the patterns and the sequences of growth. Photography has become an indispensable tool both for the documentation and for the analysis of developmental data. The present chapter assembles various photographs which illustrate the content of later chapters and which may serve both for reference and as an introduction.

The illustrations begin properly enough with a photograph of a human embryo at the postconception age of 8 weeks. This age approximately marks the time when the first overt neuromotor behavior occurs. In this first stirring, we "see" the earliest stage of the cycle of mental growth.

The growth cycle continues apace throughout the uterine period. Each week brings forth continuing but transforming patterns of behavior which constitute the action system of the baby-to-be. At a postconception age of 10 lunar months (40 weeks), the baby has reached the full-term stage of maturity which precedes birth. This stage is pictured in the transparent figure which symbolizes motherhood and which is, naturally, the central figure of an exhibit designed to portray the miracle of growth.[1]

The Book of Wisdom of the Apocrypha poetically intimates the fatefulness of the beginnings of life:

> And I also, when I was born, drew in the common air,
> And fell upon the kindred earth,
> Uttering, like all, for my first voice, the self-same wail:
> In swaddling clothes was I nursed, and with watchful cares.
> For no king had any other first beginning;
> But all men have one entrance into life, and a like departure.

Birth ushers the child into a personal world and brings him under the guiding influences of human culture. His life then becomes inextricably interwoven with the lives of those who care for him. But the basic patterning of his action system continues to be obedient to the

[1] The exhibit is part of the Medical Section in the Museum of Science and Industry, Chicago, Illinois.

same profound laws which shaped his behavior prior to birth. The presence and the power of these laws are suggested in many of the photographs which follow.

Since this is a visual chapter the reader may profit from a hint contained in a letter written by Charles Darwin when he was studying the emotional expressions of infants. He was grateful for the camera and remarked, "I find photographs made by the instantaneous process the best means of observation, as allowing more deliberation."

* * *

Perusal of the varied photographs assembled in this chapter will suggest that vision also plays an important role in the mental growth and life of the child. Our whole technology and education place a relentless premium upon alert, accurate, and swift vision.

The development of vision in the individual child is complex because it took countless ages of evolution in the race to bring vision to its present advanced state. Human visual perception ranks with speech in intricacy and passes through comparable developmental phases. Moreover, seeing is not a separate isolable function: it is profoundly integrated with the total action system of the child—his postures, his manual skills and coordination, his intelligence, and even his personality makeup. Indeed, vision is so intimately identified with the whole child that we cannot understand its economy nor its hygiene without investigating the whole child.

...or no king had any other first beginning;
...ut all men have one entrance into life,
...nd a like departure. . . .

The Wisdom of Solomon
The Apocrypha

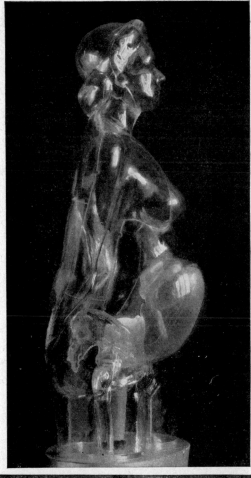

Below and right) From the exhibit "The Miracle
Growth" of the Museum of Science and Industry,
Chicago.

CHAPTER I

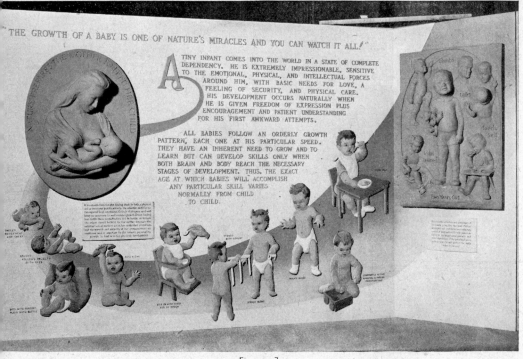

"THE GROWTH OF A BABY IS ONE OF NATURE'S MIRACLES AND YOU CAN WATCH IT ALL!"

A TINY INFANT COMES INTO THE WORLD IN A STATE OF COMPLETE DEPENDENCY. HE IS EXTREMELY IMPRESSIONABLE, SENSITIVE TO THE EMOTIONAL, PHYSICAL, AND INTELLECTUAL FORCES AROUND HIM, WITH BASIC NEEDS FOR LOVE, A FEELING OF SECURITY, AND PHYSICAL CARE. HIS DEVELOPMENT OCCURS NATURALLY WHEN HE IS GIVEN FREEDOM OF EXPRESSION PLUS ENCOURAGEMENT AND PATIENT UNDERSTANDING FOR HIS FIRST AWKWARD ATTEMPTS.

ALL BABIES FOLLOW AN ORDERLY GROWTH PATTERN, EACH ONE AT HIS PARTICULAR SPEED. THEY HAVE AN INHERENT NEED TO GROW AND TO LEARN BUT CAN DEVELOP SKILLS ONLY WHEN BOTH BRAIN AND BODY REACH THE NECESSARY STAGES OF DEVELOPMENT. THUS, THE EXACT AGE AT WHICH BABIES WILL ACCOMPLISH ANY PARTICULAR SKILL VARIES NORMALLY FROM CHILD TO CHILD.

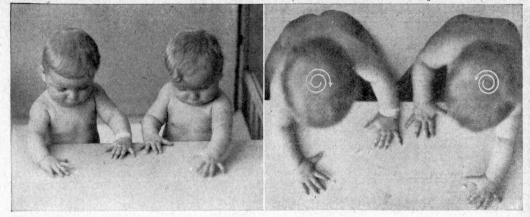

Behavior patterns of Twins T and C: Simultaneous front and overhead view of prehensory approach upon a 7 mm pellet. Note the mirror imaging of the behavior patterns; also of the crown whorls. (Twin T clockwise; Twin C counterclockwise.)

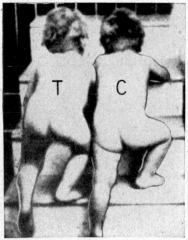

CHAPTER 5
Stair climbing behavior of Twins T and C at 79 weeks, showing similar postural adjustments.

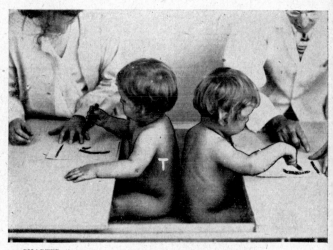

CHAPTER 5
Twins T and C at the age of 20 months. Both draw vertical stroke in response to a horizontal model.

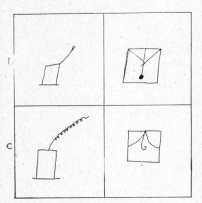

CHAPTER 5
Drawings of Twins T. and C. at 8 years and 20 years of age. Note the tendency toward curvature in Twin C as compared with Twin T.

Age 20 Years

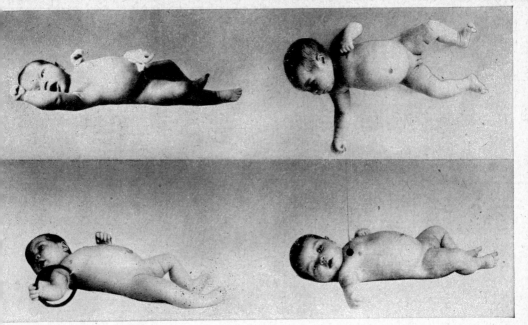

CHAPTER 7 (Fig. a)

Right tonic neck reflex consistently exhibited by infant VW at 1, 6, 8, and 12 weeks of age. This behavior pattern illustrates the developmental principle of functional asymmetry which is reflected in the construction and utilization of tools.

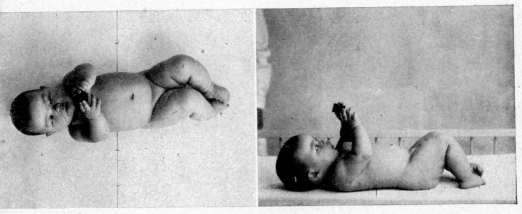

CHAPTER 7 (Fig. b)

Symmetric closing in reaction by infant VW, at age 24 weeks. A transitory stage in the development of prehension. (Simultaneous photographs taken with one camera at the zenith and the other at the horizon of the photographic dome.)

Ontogenesis of constructive activity:
a. Infant age 32 weeks, random exploitation of building blocks.
b. Infant age 18 months, tower building.
c. Age 2 years: construction of wall.
d. Age 3 years: construction of bridge.

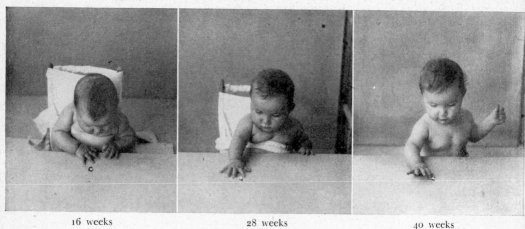

16 weeks   28 weeks   40 weeks

PELLET BEHAVIOR PATTERNS

16 weeks—Picks up pellet with eyes only
28 weeks—Rakes crudely at pellet
40 weeks—Plucks pellet with precise pincer prehension

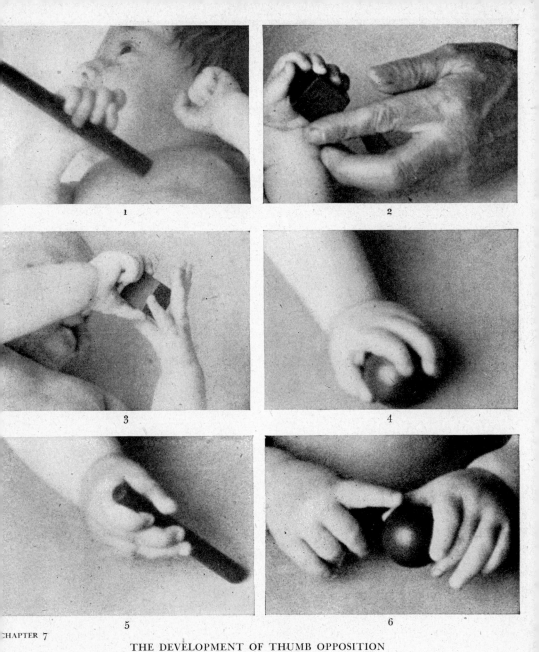

THE DEVELOPMENT OF THUMB OPPOSITION

Patterns of thumb posture typical of five maturity stages: 1. pre-pivotal adduction
(0-16 weeks) ; 2. pivoted adduction (16-28 weeks) ; 3. mesial opposition (16-28 weeks) ;
4. mesio-volar opposition (24-36 weeks) ; 5, 6. volar opposition (32-52 weeks).

NAME *Robinson, Evelyn* Boy Girl	SITUATION *2ᵈ cube*		AGE *24* Wks	
Last First				
FILM NO. *381* FILE NO. *K 117*	SERIES *Normative C* DATE *8/24/*		BY *GH*	

NOTATION	BEHAVIOR SEQUENCE	FEATURES	REGARD	SECONDS
S M P	Holds 1st cu in BH, regards	leans forward.	2nd cu	0 - 2
Phase 1	2nd cu, releases R grasp	lowers head.		
	on 1st cu, approaches	R V C loop 1.5"		
	R H to 2nd cu, bangs	contact R index		
	1st cu on TT writ L H	volar 2"		
	Approaches L H, drops cu from	L V C loop, leans R	" "	2 - 2.5
Phase 2	L H, corrals 2nd cu with			
	B H			
	Withdraws L H, grasps R	*1st grasp R H 3.5"	1st cu	2.5 - 3.5
		ulnar		
	Drags 2nd cu back and to R	Rotates 20° R, turns	2nd cu	3.5 - 5.5
	with R H, releases from	head 40° R		
	grasp 7" R, L H on TT M.			
Phase 3	is partially flexed			
Phase 4	Strikes cu L with R H	R V C sl., L V C loop	" "	5.5 - 8

Partial record of a behavior pattern analysis.

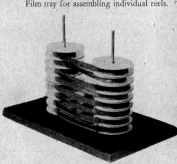

Film tray for assembling individual reels.

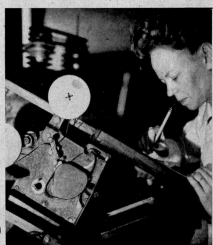

Cinema strip
showing indi-
vidual frames.

Double spindle rack for give-and-take reels.

Analytic desk showing projector and working
image.

CHAPTER 8

Specimen page of *An Atlas of Infant Behavior* illustrating the method of cinema
analysis. a) cinema strip. b) partial record of behavior analysis. c) film tray for
assembling reels. d) spindle rack for reels. e) cinemanalyzer for observing and
tracing behavior patterns.

This photographic dome was used to secure systematic cinema records of infant behavior patterns at lunar month intervals. The delineative action photographs of *An Atlas of Infant Behavior* were selected from these cinema records. Two silent cameras ride on the quadrants of the dome. The infant is examined in the crib. The dome is encased in a one way vision screen which conceals the observers from the infant but permits full view of his behavior. The photographs below delineate four phases of nine consecutive records of behavior.

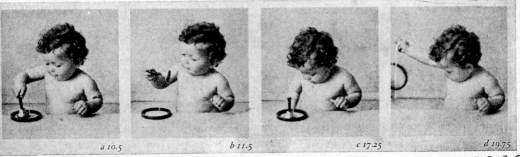

a 10.5   b 11.5   c 17.25   d 19.75

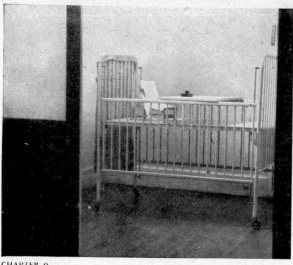
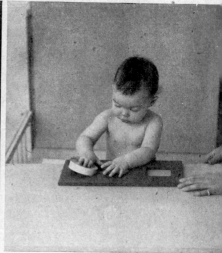

One-way-vision setup for the developmental examination of an infant and of a preschool child.

Below: a one-way-vision observation booth incorporated in a primary school room. This arrangement serves for in-training teaching and demonstration and for parent guidance.

Courtesy of The Minneapolis Tribune

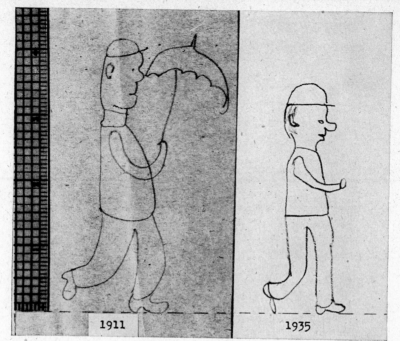

Drawings of a man made without copy by O. C. at the age of 20 years and at the age of 44 years. The reproductions were made directly from the originals. The scale at the left indicates the size of the original drawings in inches.

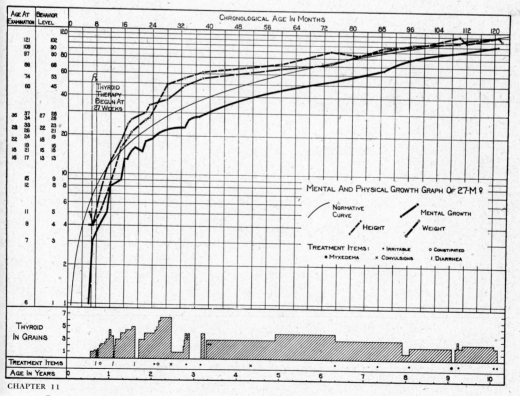

Graph showing the growth trends of 27-M from early infancy to the age of 10 years.

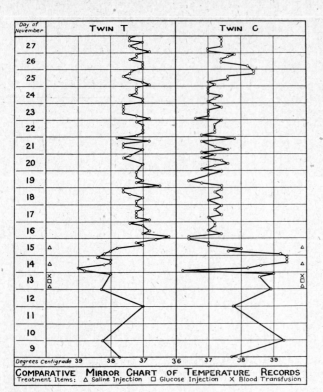

To facilitate comparisons, the temperature records of Twins T and C are charted on a mirror grid. The readings cover a period of 19 days. The infants were vaccinated on November 9. The period from November 13 to 29 was spent in a hospital, as described in the text.

COMPARATIVE MIRROR CHART OF TEMPERATURE RECORDS
Treatment Items: △ Saline Injection ☐ Glucose Injection X Blood Transfusion

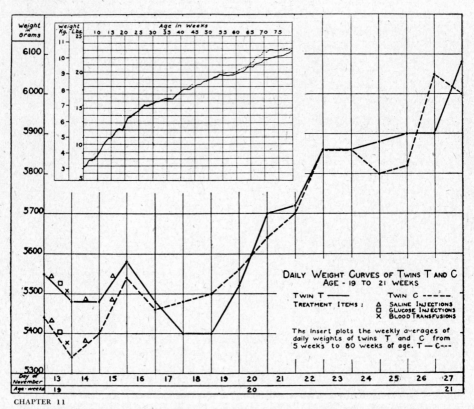

DAILY WEIGHT CURVES OF TWINS T AND C
AGE - 19 TO 21 WEEKS

TWIN T ——— TWIN C -----
TREATMENT ITEMS: △ SALINE INJECTIONS
☐ GLUCOSE INJECTIONS
X BLOOD TRANSFUSIONS

The insert plots the weekly averages of daily weights of twins T and C from 5 weeks to 80 weeks of age. T — C---

Detailed weight records of Twins T and C during their period of hospitalization. Weekly variations of daily weight for a period of 80 weeks are plotted in the inset.

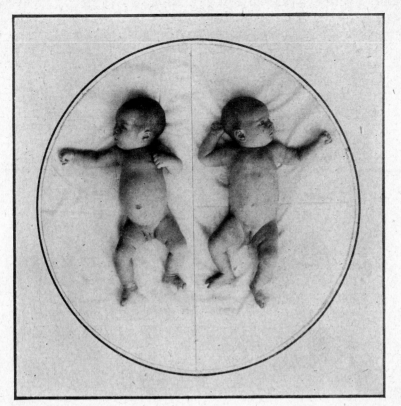

Right and left tonic-neck-reflex of normal infants (age 6 weeks) . Strongly entrenched leftward attitude a precursor of left-handedness.

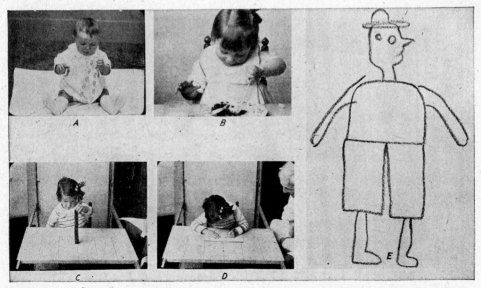

A DEEP-SEATED MOTOR TRAIT OF INDIVIDUALITY

This child showed pronounced left-handedness: a) in manipulation (age 36 weeks); b) in spoon feeding (age 80 weeks); c) in block building (age 260 weeks or 5 years); d) in drawing (also age 5 years). She draws a left-handed type of man pictured in E.

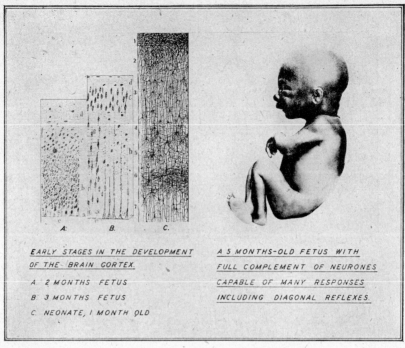

EARLY STAGES IN THE DEVELOPMENT
OF THE BRAIN CORTEX.

A 2 MONTHS FETUS

B 3 MONTHS FETUS

C NEONATE, I MONTH OLD

A 5 MONTHS-OLD FETUS WITH
FULL COMPLEMENT OF NEURONES
CAPABLE OF MANY RESPONSES
INCLUDING DIAGONAL REFLEXES.

Fig 1. The Fetal Nervous System. Five-month-old fetus with full complement of neurones capable of many responses, including diagonal reflexes. Early stages in the development of the brain cortex. a) 2 months fetus. b) 3 months fetus. c) neonate, 1 month.

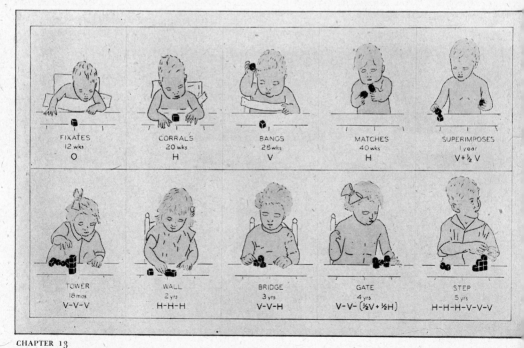

Fig. 2. The geometry of growth. Developmental progressions of exploitation in vertical, horizontal, and oblique sectors of space.

Fig. 3. These drawings were made by Y. Z., a child whose grandfather and great-uncle both were artists. The mother reports that she has given no instruction, but that the child at an early age was much devoted to working with crayon. The drawing of a man at 3 years and 5 months is already at the 5 year level. The similar drawings at 3 years and 6 months and at 3 years and 7 months show rapid increase in her abilities. Her first effort at drawing in profile occurred at the exceptionally early age of 3 years and 7 months.

bŏve) Fig. 4. Ironic fashion figure.

ight) Fig. 5. Free fluent rendering by P. Z., age 42 onths, of Peter Peter Pumpkin Eater and Peter Rabbit.

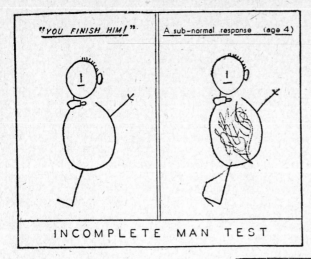

Fig. 7. The Incomplete Man Text, showing subnormal, average and advanced responses.

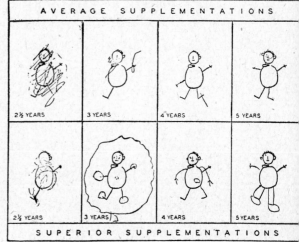

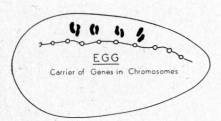

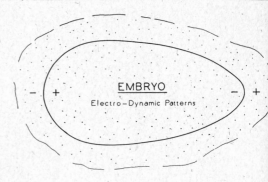

Fig. 6. The Incomplete Man Text, developmental determinants.

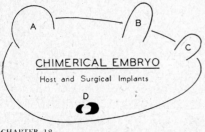

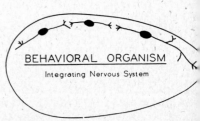

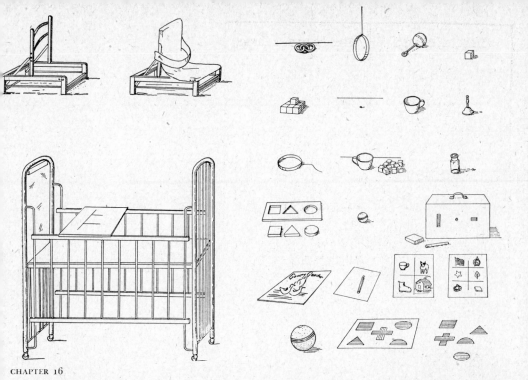

Right: Examination materials: tricolored rings, dangling ring, rattle, cube, massed cubes, pellet, cup, bell, ring and string, cup and cubes, pellet and bottle, formboard, ball, performance box with block and rod, picture book, paper and crayon, picture cards, large ball, color forms.

Left (top): Examination chair for young infants. The chair is provided with a washable and removable canvas covering. The infant is secured in position by a broad canvas band.

Left (bottom): Clinical crib for developmental examinations. The crib is of the ordinary hospital type with adjustable side panels. A sturdy wooden platform replaces the springs. A removable wooden table top spans the top rails of the panels.

CHAPTER 16

A suite for the developmental examination of infants and preschool children.

Assume a child of preschool age, accompanied by a nurse or mother. The child enters at (1), passes through the hallway (2) which connects with the reception room (3) and also with the bathroom at (6). The reception room is furnished with adult chairs and a play pen (4) and child's chair (5). The observation room (7) has been partially darkened by drawing the shade at the window. The recorder takes station in the chair equipped with writing arm (9). Observers can be seated nearby, behind the one-way-vision screen window (12) which communicates with the examination room (15), entered by the door at (13), also equipped with one-way-vision window (14). The examination room is equipped with an examination table (16) showing the picture book (17) and child's chair (18) in position. The mother sits at the right (19); the examiner at the left (20), with direct access to the examining cabinet (21).

If the child is of infant age, the same facilities are used in a slightly different manner. Room 7 becomes the examining room and room 15 the observer's and recorder's room. The one-way-vision screen window in the communicating door (12) operates equally well in the reverse direction. The examining crib is moved to a favorable position.

DOWN.
BECKENHAM, KENT.
(RAILWAY STATION
ORPINGTON. S.E.R.)

CHAPTER 3

Page one and page eight of a letter written by Charles Darwin to Mrs. Emily Talbot, Secretary of the Education Depart...

PART ONE
Methods of Approach

Charles Darwin and Child Development

"Without doubt the first three!" This was the emphatic answer which Charles Darwin gave when as an old man he was asked which years of life he considered the most "subject to incubative impressions." There is much evidence that he was deeply intrigued by the phenomena of human infancy.

Darwin's mind ranged over all natural phenomena—geology, botany, zoology, anthropology. The same passionate inquisitiveness as to the genesis of things which caused him to spend years of exacting study on his "beloved barnacles" led him also to set down abundant notes on the behavior of his babies. He was the father of ten—six sons and four daughters, born within a period of seventeen years. The tenderness and sympathetic insight he displayed as a parent are well known. Less recognized is the significance of his work in the scientific study of child development.

Human infancy is full of enigma. Grave perplexities arose in the minds of pre-Darwinian theologians who tried to explain the imperfection, or as they called it, "the pettishness" of childhood. The problem of crying troubled the discussions of hereditary guilt. Saint Augustine insisted that the crying of a baby is *not* sinful, and therefore does not deserve eternal damnation. We shall see, presently, how Darwin approached this ancient riddle of the infant's cry.

Darwin's perplexities were those of a naturalist. His mind had a scientist's "naked need for ideological order." This order he tirelessly sought.

My first notebook (on the transmutation of species) was opened in July 1837. I worked on true Baconian principles and without any theory collected facts on a wholesale scale. . . . In October 1838, that is fifteen months after I had begun my systematic enquiry, I happened to read for amusement Malthus on Population. . . . My first child was born on December 27, 1839, and I at once commenced to make notes on the first dawn of the various experiences which he exhibited, for I felt convinced, even at this early period, that the most complex and fine shades of expression must all have had a gradual and natural origin.

From the foregoing dates it is clear that the study of infant behavior very early contributed to the formation of Darwin's ideas. He converted the enigma of infancy into one more touchstone for understanding the origin of species. Much as he admired Sir Charles Bell's writings, he could not believe, with Bell, that man had been created with certain muscles specially adapted for the expression of feelings.

And so Darwin began a series of observations and even a few benign experiments on his newborn son, "Doddy."

On the seventh day I touched the naked sole of his foot with a bit of paper, and he jerked it away, curling at the same time his toes, like a much older child when tickled. The perfection of these reflex movements shows that the extreme imperfection of the voluntary ones is not due to the state of the muscles or of the coordinating centers, but to that of the seat of the will. . . .

When this child was about four months old, I made in his presence many odd noises and strange grimaces, and tried to look savage; but the noises, if not too loud, as well as the grimaces, were all taken as good jokes; and I attributed this at the time to their being preceded or accompanied by smiles. When five months old, he seemed to understand a compassionate expression and tone of voice.

The recorded observations of Darwin's infant covered a wide range of subjects such as vision, winking, hearing, anger, fear, pleasurable sensations, affection, association of ideas, reason, left-handedness, moral sense, unconsciousness, shyness, language, sympathy. Thirty-seven years later (1877) the diary records reappeared as "A Biographic Sketch of an Infant," published in *Mind*, the British Quarterly Review of Psychology and Philosophy. The manuscript was submitted to the editor with characteristic self-deprecation: "I cannot judge whether it is worth publishing, from having been so much interested in watching the dawn of the several faculties in my own infant."[1] Darwin was remembering the "fine degree of paternal fervour" which had prompted him as a young father and scientist to declare, "I had not the smallest conception there was so much in a five-month baby."

Darwin's observations of infants were by no means limited to his first-born. He renewed his observations on Doddy's brothers and sisters, concentrating on the characteristics of instinctive and emotional behavior. The most valuable and systematic data were incorporated in his famous essay on "The Expression of the Emotions in Man and Animals" (1872). Darwin had first intended to treat the subject in a single chapter of his *Descent of Man*, but the essay inevitably expanded into a book—a book which a theological reviewer immediately described as "the most powerful and insidious of all the author's works."

This volume exhibited in an eminent degree, as his friend A. R. Wallace remarked, the author's restless curiosity and an insatiable longing to discover underlying causes. Darwin left no stone unturned in his search for data. He carried on a heavy correspondence, circulating printed inquiries among physiologists, physicians, and missionaries, on items such as follow: (11) Is extreme fear expressed in the same general manner as with Europeans? (4) Do the children when sulky, pout or greatly protrude the lips? (16) Is the head nodded vertically in affirmation, and shaken laterally in negation?

Nothing better illustrates Darwin's method of investigation and his outlook on the phenomena of child development than his studies of

[1] Darwin added that he would never have thought of sending the manuscript had not an article by M. Taine appeared in translation in an earlier issue of *Mind*. When Taine contributed the original article, "The Acquisition of Language by Children," to the *Revue philosophique* (January 1876) he commented that his observations had been interrupted by the calamities of the year 1870—calamities that are now repeating themselves, less than seventy years later.

the age-old problem of infant crying. He observed frowning, pouting, screaming, tears, weeping in his own children. He plied his friends to make similar observations. In a letter to Huxley he asks Mrs. Huxley "to look out when one of her children is struggling and just going to burst out crying." And he adds, "A dear young lady near here plagued a very young child for my sake, till he cried, and I saw the eyebrows for a second or two beautifully oblique, just before the torrent of tears began. . . ."

Far from being a trivial incidental, the obliquing of the eyebrows and the contraction of the muscles around the eyes became a topic of persistent research. He analyzed Duchenne's photographic records of the facial muscles under galvanic stimulation. He consulted paintings and sculptures. He gathered data from asylums for the insane. He enlisted keepers of the zoo and he also closely watched his own cats and dogs. From London and Hamburg he secured photographs of crying children, many made expressly for him. (He remarks, "I found photographs made by the instantaneous process the best means of observation, as allowing more deliberation." How he would have delighted in the delineations of cinema records had they been available to him!)

Probing deeper into the physiology of the weeping eye he enlisted the help of Professor Donders, of Utrecht, who carried through an elaborate experimental study on the action of the eyelids in the determination of blood flow from expiratory effort. Even after the publication of the volume on *Expression of the Emotions*, Darwin kept in touch with Donders, pursuing still further the problem of orbicular contraction. "I think," he writes, "it would be worth while to ascertain whether those born blind, when young, and whilst screaming violently contract the muscles round the eyes like ordinary infants. And, secondly, whether in afteryears they rarely or never frown." Always alert to alternative possibilities, he continued with characteristic avidity for facts, "If it should prove true that infants born blind do not contract their orbicular muscles whilst screaming (though I can hardly believe it) it would be interesting to know whether they shed tears as copiously as other children."

It was not Darwin's habit to terminate his investigations. Soon after publication he began to revise his volume on *Expression*. His cousin, Galton, called attention to an omission. "Was it not universal among blubbering children (when not trying to see if harm or help was coming out of the corner of one eye) of pressing the knuckles against the eyeballs, thereby reinforcing the orbicularis?" Almost apologetically, Darwin says he should have thought of this point. "As far as my memory serves, they do not do so whilst roaring, in which case compression would be of no use. I think it is at the close of the crying fit, as if they wished to stop their eyes crying, or possibly to relieve the irritation from salt tears. I wish I knew more about knuckles and crying."

Darwin's approach to the problem of child behavior is comparative. He is equally interested in the pouting of the European child, of Kafir, Fingo, Malay, Abyssinian, orang, and chimpanzee. He finds that discontented primates protrude their lips to an extraordinary degree, Europeans to a lesser degree, but that among young children lip protrusion is characteristic of sulkiness throughout the greater part of the world. He felt certain that our progenitors protruded their lips when sulky and disappointed. Indeed, the study of emotional expression strengthened the conclusion that man is derived from some lower animal form.

Comparative psychology today has taken on a limited connotation which makes it almost synonymous with animal psychology. For Darwin, the naturalist, comparative psychology was more capacious; it was truly comparative. He was primarily interested in phyletic implications, and the breadth of Romanes' work in this field appealed to him. In a letter (to Romanes, 1878) he compared half playfully, half seriously, the intellect of a young monkey and that of his 2-year-old grandchild (Frank's son). He saw in the thinking of deaf-mutes "one of the richest of all mines, worth working carefully for years, and very deeply." Again, half seriously, half humorously, he relayed a significant suggestion to Romanes: "Frank says you ought to keep an idiot, a deaf-mute, a monkey, and a baby in your house!"

Darwin was not a psychologist, but he had already inaugurated concepts of life and growth which were to revolutionize the psychological formulations of child development. He profoundly influenced G. Stanley Hall, a young scientist who became a powerful exponent of Darwinism in America. With fertile suggestiveness and comprehensiveness, Hall applied the concepts of evolution to the mind of the child and of the race. Hall also became the father of a nationwide child-study movement which liberalized elementary education and led to scientific advances in the study of child development.

This movement in its mixture of empirical fact finding and zeal for social welfare was characteristically American. It began to take definite shape in the early '80's. Vast areas of prejudice and ignorance had to be overcome; but this did not dampen the ardor of the pioneers who, as we shall see, called upon Darwin for help, the year before he died at Down.

The American Social Science Association had just been founded. In 1881, Mrs. Emily Talbot, enterprising secretary of its education department, issued a circular in which she referred to the new investigative spirit of the time,

... the intelligence of animals, even coming in for a due share of attention. ... Recently, some educators in this country have been thinking that to study the natural development of a single child is worth more than a Noah's Ark full of animals. ... In this belief the Education Department of the American Social Science Association has issued the accompanying Register, and asks the parents of very young children to interest themselves in the subject—

1. By recognizing the importance of the study of the youngest infants. 2. By observing the simplest manifestations of their life and movements. 3. By answering fully and carefully the questions asked in the Register. 4. By a careful record of the signs of development during the coming year, each observation to be verified if possible by other members of the family. 5. By interesting their friends in the subject and forwarding the results to the Secretary. 6. Above all, by perseverance and exactness in recording these observations.

From the records of many thousand observers in the next few years it is believed that important facts will be gathered of great value to the educator and to the psychologist. . . .

This ambitious program did not, however, fail to awaken some resistance and satire. Noah's Ark was still far from a metaphor to large sections of the population who fumed or laughed at Charles Darwin, author, in 1859, of that shocking, green-covered volume entitled, *The Origin of Species*. As late as 1889, a lecture on "The Scientific Study of Infant Intelligence" proved a popular success by reason of the fun it poked at the new child study. (The lecture was given in "The Mechanics Course" of the Sheffield Scientific School of Yale University, and some months later before the Scientific Society of Bridgeport, Connecticut, by Henry T. Blake.)

With devastating good nature, the lecturer cited the assiduous experiments of Professor Preyer, Monsieur Perez, Herr Kussmaul and Dr. Darwin, with repeated ironic reference to the doctor's family pride in his simian tree-dwelling forefathers. Referring to the registers of the American Social Science Association, the lecturer concluded:

The registers will go like *la grippe* into every house. Mothers, sisters, aunts, grandfathers, of course, possibly even fathers, will engage in the scientific study of infant intelligence, and the merits of the newly born generation will be rolled into the fold of a permanent record with as much precision and certainty as we used to operate last year's puzzle of "The-little-pigs-in-clover." Every properly constituted University and every Scientific Association will have its cradle of science and its baby chair of philosophy. Under the stimulus of registration also, a vast improvement may be hoped for in the quality of the registered article.

This ridicule was entertaining, and not always amiss. But today the ironic prophecy has a new irony—it has come true: Every well-constituted university in America now has a chair or courses in child psychology, and a nursery school for preschool children has almost become a standard feature of the academic campus.

Charles Darwin took the American Social Science Association Register of Infant Development more seriously than our popular lecturer.

With a courtesy which was typical of him, he addressed a lengthy letter to Secretary Emily Talbot. This letter is so revealing that it is here reproduced in full.[2]

Down
Beckenham, Kent
Railway Station
Orpington, S.E.R.

July 19" 1881

Dear Madam

In response to your wish I have much pleasure in expressing the interest which I feel in your proposed investigation on the mental & bodily development of infants.—Very little is at present accurately known on this subject, & I believe that isolated observations will add but little to our knowledge, whereas tabulated results from a very large number of observations systematically made, would perhaps throw much light on the sequence & period of development of the several faculties. This knowledge would probably give a foundation for some improvement in our education of young children, & would show us whether the same system ought to be followed in all cases.

I will venture to specify a few points of enquiry which, as it seems to me, possess some scientific interest. For instance does the education of the parents influence the mental powers of their children at any age, either at a very early or somewhat more advanced stage? This could perhaps be learnt by school-masters or mistresses, if a large number of children were first classed according to age & their mental attainments, & afterwards in accordance with the education of their parents, as far as this could be discovered. As observation is one of the earliest faculties developed in young children, & as their power would probably be exercised in an equal degree by the children of educated & un-educated persons, it seems improbable that any transmitted effect from education would be displayed only at a somewhat advanced age. It would be desirable to test statistically in a similar manner the truth of the often repeated statement that colored children at first learn as quickly as white children, but that they afterwards fall off in progress. If it could be proved that education acts not only on the individual, but by transmission on the race, this would be a great encouragement to all working on this all-important subject.

It is well known that children sometimes exhibit at a very early age strong special tastes, for which no cause can be assigned, although occasionally they may be accounted for by reversion to the taste or occupation of some progenitor; & it would be interesting to learn how far such early tastes are persistent &

[2] The original eight-page letter in Darwin's own hand is now in the possession of Professor Marion Talbot, daughter of Mrs. Emily Talbot, who kindly provided us with a photostatic reproduction.

influence the future career of the individual. In some instances such tastes die away without apparently leaving any after effect; but it would be advisable to know how far this is commonly the case; as we should then know whether it were important to direct, as far as this is possible, the early tastes of our children. It may be more beneficial that a child should follow energetically some pursuit, of however trying a nature, and thus acquire perseverance, than that he should be turned from it, because of no future advantage to him.

I will mention one other such point of enquiry in relation to very young children, which may possibly prove important with respect to the origin of language; but it could be investigated only by persons possessing an accurate musical ear. Children even before they can articulate express some of their feelings & desires by noises uttered in different notes. For instance they make an interrogative noise, & others of assent and dissent in different tones, & it would, I think, be worth while to ascertain whether there is any uniformity in different children in the pitch of their voices under various frames of mind.

I fear that this letter can be of no use to you, but it will serve to show my sympathy & good wishes in your researches.

I beg leave to remain

Dear Madam
Yours faithfully
CHARLES DARWIN

To Mrs. EMILY TALBOT.—

The most concrete contribution that Darwin made to the embryonic science of child psychology was embodied in his volume on *Expression of Emotions*. Here he deployed his genius as a naturalist with the same penetration he brought to bear on barnacles, coral atolls, orchids, and earthworms. He did not set himself up as a psychologist; indeed he never entirely escaped a certain naive dualism in his views of the human mind. But it was as a naturalist that he addressed himself to the far-reaching problems of fear, rage, and affection. He attacked them with a boldness, objectivity, and freshness which make much present-day discussion of similar subjects seem somewhat anemic in comparison. We may well go back to Darwin for vitalization of outlook and even of method. For the scientific study of child development is in need of the naturalist's breadth of vision.

The year 1939 marks a significant anniversary. It was exactly one hundred years ago that Darwin first clearly conceived his epoch-making theory. His chief contribution to the intellectual thought of his time lay in his perception of the gradual genesis of all living things, including the genesis of the human mind. The developmental outlook upon nature and upon its vast web of organic life led to profound revisions in the interpretation of childhood. The concept of evolution with all its corollaries introduced a new and humanizing kind of relativity. Even New England divines, still wrestling with Calvinistic and Augustinian ideas of original sin, softened their doctrines of infant baptism. The new naturalism proved to be a solvent of the gloomier beliefs of fixity and fate. So pervading was Darwin's influence that it has been said that he won for man absolute freedom in the study of the laws of nature.

Without that freedom it would be impossible to penetrate into the meaning of human infancy and into the nature of child development. The modern scientific study of child development is in itself a social assertion of a free spirit of truth. If that spirit is trammeled in any way, man will never know himself, because to know himself he must understand clearly the processes by which he came to be, the processes of child development. So we can scarcely err in paying tribute to Charles Darwin, remover of trammels, even though we realize that science in its most organic sense is a social phenomenon, a cultural product. Darwin, more than any other single individual, initiated the genetic rationalism which now characterizes the investigation of human infancy.

CHAPTER IV

A Biological Psychology*

We are met to inaugurate a museum of psychology. May I begin by quoting a letter which I recently received from a spirited adolescent girl, age 14? "I have many hobbies," she wrote, "in fact they are almost countless. The one I like best is keeping a museum. As you probably remember, our house is quite large. My museum (the name of it is 'A Country Museum') is one of the smaller rooms upstairs. . . . Some of the things are Indian arrow heads, a tip of an Indian ax, a hornet's nest, and some butterflies. The thing that I thought would be interesting is to try to get a stone or two from every state of the union. . . ." So I sent her a rock from Connecticut.

There is a good deal of psychology in that letter; not so much in the rock itself. A psychological museum must deal with phenomena less substantial and less accessible than rocks and hornet nests. Can it succeed in giving tangibleness to the human mind? The Lewis Institute, your trustees, and director have undertaken a project of great difficulty, but one which has important pioneering possibilities. Museums have in general been devoted to the products and often to the curiosities of human culture. A psychological museum will have to concern itself in a new way with a delineation of the nature, mechanisms, and the needs of human behavior. It will have to design a new kind of trans-

* Address delivered at inauguration of Psychological Museum, Garfield Park, Chicago, May 4, 1938.

parent man. Its problem is to objectify, to make visible, the operations and the laws of the human mind, to give us an inside look. In this age of photography, of pictorial journalism and of the motion picture, of window displays and of murals, the race wishes to see with its own eyes, to look. More eagerly than ever, we are trying to get glimpses of ourselves.

Ancient man was moved by similar impulses. When he scratched and daubed his own murals of a bison hunt on the walls of a cave, he got a little further outside of himself and a better perspective upon himself. This was his art gallery and museum. But his psychology was crude. He had only the dimmest notion of his mental life and the mental life of others. He was confused by the echo in the valley, by the reflection of his own image on the water surface, by vapor and wind. He could not have understood William James's chapter on "The Stream of Consciousness," even if it had been translated into Neanderthal. (But even William James is rather recent, for it was only seventy years ago that he returned to America from Germany with tidings of a possible science of the mind.)

Savage man is to this day literally afraid of his own shadow. He regards his shadow as his very soul, or as a vital part of himself. The natives of Nias, Frazer tells us, tremble at the sight of a rainbow, because they think it is a net spread by a powerful spirit to catch their shadows.

Modern science has done something for us. It has at least explained the optics and the physics of the rainbow. And at long last, science is also removing some of the lingering terrors and mysteries of the human soul.

Psychology used to be defined as the science of the human soul. It makes little difference if we substitute the words human mind or human behavior. It is an error, however, to think of psychology as *the* science of the mind—as the one and only science of the mind. The organization of modern sciences is such that no one science can be allocated to a distinct and detached province. This is particularly true of the life sciences and their subdivisions. Only the dictionary maker can draw sharp cleavages today between physics, chemistry, biology, physiology, and psychology. The whole trend of contemporary science is toward hyphenation and interpenetration. Johns Hopkins recently created a chair of physiological anatomy. Some time ago such a hybrid would have been regarded as grotesque. Today we grant that static phenomena can be studied in the making. We also recognize that the most creative advances of science take place at the growing margins where diverse fields of science touch each other and lose their separate identities. The tendency toward excessive specialization is counterbalanced by a tendency toward hyphenation which brings disciplines into union. Witness psychobiology, neuropsychiatry, biophysics, psychosomatics, etc.

Paradoxically, the highest reaches in specialization require the profoundest fathoming into fundamentals. W. B. Hardy, for example, we are informed, started his career as a biologist but ended as a physicist, studying the phenomena of lubrication and the molecular structure of silk and wool fibers. Did he go astray? Not if we grant that the characteristics of protoplasm remain a mystery without a thorough knowledge of viscosity. We can not even be certain that he has not made an ultimate contribution to psychology, via the study of lubrication! Such roundabout implication and deviousness of approach are in fact characteristic of the structure or rather the physiological anatomy of modern science.

Diverse sciences show a tendency to interpenetrate. This is peculiarly true of the study of the human mind. The psyche, the behavior of a man, is a focal manifestation of the "forces" of nature. Man is part of the order of nature, the same order which determines the differential elasticity of silk and wool fibers and the stripes of the rainbow. His psychology is an integrated expression of all the factors that contribute to the ordering of life. Neither the integration nor the factors can be comprehended by traveling the narrow trail of a single scientific discipline.

[47]

There are, accordingly, many scientific approaches to the problems of human psychology. I use the term approaches deliberately to suggest the broader avenues which lead to the central city of Man-Soul. The term is not necessarily synonymous with method. An approach is a pathway; a method is a manner of procedure by which you travel. Statistical method, for example, represents a tool, a mathematical device for the clarification and formulation of data rather than the creation of data. The experimental method, when it deals with crucial and predictive issues, is in many respects supreme. We are inclined to agree with Boring's contention that "the application of the experimental method to the problem of mind is the great outstanding event in the history of the study of the mind, an event to which no other is comparable."

It does not follow, however, that the science of the human mind has depended, or will depend, entirely upon direct experimentation with specific psychological phenomena. More than any other science, psychology will be derived from basic, contributive disciplines which deal with the subordinate but determining orders of nature. The science of psychology will continue to grow by a social process of accrual. It will advance on tidal currents generated by the basic sciences. Already it has burst the confines of a somewhat conventionalized series of textbooks. At the moment we do not so much need a genius who will make original experimental discoveries in the realm of mind. Rather we need a Darwin who will reveal, co-ordinate, and consolidate the unlabeled psychological knowledge which has already accrued, but has not yet become intellectually integrated.

There are at least five fundamental approaches to the comprehensive science of the mind, and none of these is purely psychological. From a monistic standpoint of determinism, we need not insist too rigidly upon distinctions between mind and matter or between structure and function. We are obliged to reckon with all forms of relatedness which truly reflect the universal order and the regulatory principles that pervade alike animate and inanimate nature. Without aiming at symmetrical emphasis, our comments will deal with (1) Neurophysiology, (2) Chemistry, (3) Clinical Studies, (4) Developmental Morphology, (5) Cultural Anthropology. More direct and introspective approaches we shall not attempt to consider.

(1) *Neurophysiology.* Scientific psychology arose within the domain of physiology. Must it not always have a deep root in the physiology of the nervous system? For the nervous system supports and serves the fundamental functions of sensation and movement, which constitute the very essence of mind. To be sure you can not adequately "represent thoughts and emotions as nerve cells tickling one another." E. W. Scripture in a moment of autobiographic candor went on to say, "I throw aside every book on psychology the moment I see a picture of the brain in it." We cannot, however, find support for this bit of Scripture in the writings of Sir Charles Bell, Johannes Müller, Magnus, Pavlov, Sherrington, or Lashley.

Sechenov in 1863, in a famous lecture on "The Reflexes of the Brain," initiated a new chapter in science. "All psychical acts without exception," he boldly asserted, "if they are not complicated by elements of emotion, are developed by means of reflexes." From this thesis have sprung some two thousand published studies of the conditioned reflex, with titles ranging from *The Withdrawal of the Tubeworm from a Shadow* to *The Investigatory Reflex of Homo Sapiens.*

Neurophysiology is today one of the most active fields of hyphenated science. The techniques are becoming increasingly refined. A century and a quarter ago it was an epoch-making discovery to make a simple distinction between the sensory and motor roots of the spinal cord. Today the almost infinitesimal currents of nerves and nerve centers are registered, their rhythms photographed in curves of beautiful precision. With devices for both auditory and visual magnification, the electrometry of the brain has swiftly amassed voluminous data—more in fact than the investigatory cerebrum can immediately cope with. By the method of thermocoagulation, individual layers of the brain cortex are being separately explored. By means of ultra delicate probing, microscopic groups of nerve cells are being identified in the medulla. Such researches are destined to give us an intimate knowledge of the architecture of the nervous system, and this knowledge will make our concepts of human behavior more deterministic and mechanistic in the best scientific sense.

It can scarcely be argued that these neurophysiological studies lie too deep below the threshold of consciousness and outside the scope of psychology. Even in the detailed studies of animal respiration, it has been found that no two dogs breathe exactly alike. Individual differences in dogs and man must be studied on a neurophysiological level.

The work and the career of George E. Coghill furnish solid evidence of the scientific significance of the neurophysiological approach. His primary interest was psychological, but even as a graduate student he says, "I became aware that the natural approach to the kind of psychological information I wanted lay through the physiology of the nervous system. Obviously, also, the physiology of the nervous system must be approached through its anatomy, about which I knew nothing." So for thirty years or more he has been making minute studies of the genetic and functional histology of *amblystoma,* a mere mud puppy. Did he go astray?

Although Coghill has not made a single experiment in psychology, in the orthodox sense, he has already had a profound influence on the biological interpretation of psychological problems. His three lectures on "Anatomy and the Problem of Behavior," delivered in London, bid fair to become classic. The thin volume which contains them belongs on a five-foot shelf.

(2) *Chemistry.* Chemistry is one domain of science which is certain to make epochal progress during the next few decades. And this progress, we may well believe, will reshape our concepts and control of human behavior. The Associated Press, in its report of the recent meeting of the American Chemical Society, characterized the newly purified protein, prolactin, as "this mother-instinct-crystal." Here we have hyphenation with a vengeance, but with more than journalistic

justification, for it is literally true that this chemical substance releases, sustains, and intensifies fundamental emotional reaction in different species equipped with mammary glands. (The newspaper headlines were startling enough: "Yale hormone makes tom cats give milk and roosters brood!")

Osler, in a more than humorous aside, while lecturing on endocrinology, told his audience that their ability to listen to his lecture depended upon the functioning at that very moment of their thyroid glands. These glands secrete thyroxine, a substance which is inextricably bound up with the phenomena of attention and memory, growth and learning. A universal history of psychology would have to give a place of honor to Kendall, who isolated thyroxine in 1918.

To illustrate the psychological implications, I may cite an illustration. For a period of twelve years we have followed the mental development of a girl who was diagnosed as a cretin in early infancy. She was fed thyroxine at the age of 6 months. She has attained a normal level of intelligence, thanks to the thyroxine which she has taken regularly all these years, with one exception. At the age of 9 years temporary myxedema developed, due to a pharmaceutical error. The druggist having made a mistake, she was fed for one month on thymus rather than thyroid substance. Cretinous signs at once emerged, but retreated as soon as thyroxine was substituted. This child's psychology literally hangs on a thyroid thread, and in observing her we have acquired a healthy respect for the chemical basis of mental life.

The pharmacopoeia lists an amazing number of drugs which have psychological effects. Someday no doubt the mechanism of these effects will be better understood in terms of molecules, atoms, chemical mosaics, and chemical configurations. Neurophysiological processes will be conceived chemically. Already they are being envisaged in terms of electrochemistry and the distribution of electric potentials.

The ordering factors of life are at bottom chemical, whether they be subatomic, atomic, molecular, colloidal, paracrystalline, or anatomical. These chemical factors probably even determine the Gestalten of psychology. There is, in the words of Needham, "a hierarchical continuity." Biochemistry is increasingly concerned with the morphology as well as the constituency of matter, and is bridging the gulf between sciences of matter and of form: ". . . the fields of morphology and biochemistry are not so sundered as is often supposed. Organizing relations are found at the molecular level and at the colloidal and paracrystalline level, as well as at the anatomical level. Hardy's work, far from showing that no structure existed in the cell, showed on the contrary how subtle it must be. Although we are still in the earliest historical stages of any far-reaching organization-calculus, we can yet see that biological order, like (but very much more complicated than) crystal order, is a natural consequence of the properties of matter, and one characteristic mode of their manifestation."

Needham should be able to speak with authority, for he has compiled three scholarly volumes entitled *Chemical Embryology*. Is it not probable that someday we may have an equally monumental work on Chemical Psychology?

(3) *Clinical Studies.* Under this heading we wish to stress the importance of clinical materials and naturalistic data rather than the peculiar merits of clinical procedure. There is no occasion to make an invidious distinction between clinical and experimental methods. Each may reinforce the other. Healthy progress in experimental medicine depends upon corrective contacts with the realities of clinical medicine. The same interdependence holds for clinical and experimental forms of psychology.

There is a whole host of "experiments" which no scientist has the ingenuity to plan nor the gift to perform. Nature performs them and presents them to him as riddles to solve. They take the shape of monsters, of freaks, of abnormal, eccentric, atypical individuals. The anomalies and the deviations may involve the total organism, they may involve only a sector or a small phase. In such moments of abnormality, as Goethe once remarked, Nature reveals her secrets. That is, she reveals them if we meet the challenge and make sufficient effort to explain her experimental vagary.

The feebleminded, the insane, the psychopathic, the genius, will always provide rich materials which can be encompassed only by expert familiarity, by a naturalistic feeling for reality, and by intuitive insight. Let us not underrate the vast opportunities for productive interpretation. "It would seem," as Wilfred Trotter says in an acute article in the *British Medical Journal,* "that it must be an advantage to an experimental science to have an observational side, the function of which, in addition to its use as an implement of research, would chiefly be to promote the atmosphere of intellectual liveliness which is so important as evidence of health."

The unusual elucidates the usual, the abnormal helps to define the normal, because one is a variant or exaggeration of the other. There is one type of clinical material which furnishes extraordinary opportunity for controlled, comparative observation because it comes in pairs; namely, twins. Twins are interesting in their own right, but scientifically they are most significant when used as touchstones for the elucidation of biological and psychological phenomena.

The *method of co-twin control* is an experimental device for analyzing biogenetic problems, with special reference to mental growth, learning, and individuality. Twins, particularly young monozygotic twins, are almost made to order for such biogenetic studies. In identical twins, nature provides a stage for comparatively observing the effects of a developmental stimulus which may be deliberately confined to one twin. By comprehensive cross reference, the co-twin becomes a control and a check both upon observation and conclusions. This method reaches its greatest efficiency when a high degree of correspondence has been established by careful measurements prior to the experimental observations. Careless use of the method and failure to define thoroughgoing comparisons in advance should be deprecated.

The method has a certain statistical validity, even when confined to a single pair of twins. The "statistical" validity resides in the numerousness of the physical, biochemical, and developmental corre-spondences which are so extensively present in monozygotic twins. The correspondences are sometimes so refined as to be little short of un-canny, as witness the exquisite similarities of twin electro-encephalo-grams. Where else in nature or in the samplings of the laboratory can we match in scope and detail the biological equivalence of identical twins?

From a research standpoint we need not unduly deplore the fact that quintuplets occur only once in 19,698,322 pregnancies. Twins we shall always have with us in ample numbers of highly similar pairs for clinical and experimental studies.

(4) *Developmental Morphology.* In the study of the human mind one can not escape problems of pattern and form. When Goethe coined the word *Morphologie,* he was interested in the forms of flowers and skulls. To this day the term carries physical connotations. But the concepts of morphology can be extended to the phenomena of be-havior. Morphology is the science of form. Let the dictionary remind us that form is the shape of anything as distinguished from the sub-stance of that thing. Behavior has shape.

The shapes which behaviors assume can be investigated in their own scientific right. A morphological approach leads to the description and measurement of specific forms; the systematic study of topographic relations and correlations of such forms, their ontogenetic progression and involution; their comparative features among individuals and among species.

"Structure is only the intimate expression of function," was a leading maxim of John Hunter. In a monistic (but not mystic) sense "the mind" may be regarded as a living, growing "structure," even though it lacks corporeal tangibility. It is a complex, organizing action system which manifests itself in characteristic forms of behavior—in patterns of posture, locomotion, prehension, manipulation, of perception, com-munication, and social response. The action systems of embryo, fetus, infant, and child undergo pattern changes which are so sequential that we may be certain that the patterning process is governed by mechanisms of form regulation—the same mechanisms which are being established by the science of embryology.

Experimental embryology is now one of the most active and flourishing of all the life sciences. It has undertaken the analysis of development, particularly as it affects the anatomy of the organism. But the investigators are increasingly using functional and behavior criteria to define the somatic anatomy. This is natural, for by the principle of hierarchical continuity, there is but one physiology of development. The growth of tissues, of organs, and of behavior is obedient to identical laws of developmental morphology.

It cannot, therefore, be doubted that the general physiology of mental development will find its deeper roots in the same scientific soil which is now intensively cultivated in laboratories of experimental embryology. Already many of the current morphogenetic concepts have more than vague analogy to psychical processes: embryonic field, gradient theory, regional determination, autonomous induction, complementary induction, potency, polarity, symmetry, time correlation, etc. Associationism as a psychological tradition has come down from Aristotle and still has considerable vitality, as shown by a prodigious preoccupation with problems of learning and the conditioned reflex. Needless to say, the laws of association will someday be reformulated in terms of the biology and physiology of development. The full co-ordination of animal and human psychology will depend upon such reformulations.

A more concrete paragraph may be in order here. Take for illustration the tonic neck reflex (t.n.r.), an interesting, asymmetric pattern of behavior common to man and lower animals. Magnus discovered that when he rotated the head of an experimental rabbit, a characteristic response occurred: (a) extension of the forelimb on the side toward which the head was turned, (b) flexion of the opposite forelimb. We have found this postural attitude a ubiquitous characteristic of the human infant in the first 3 months of life. It is his preferred posture, as he lies supine, awake, head averted. By the age of 20 weeks, his head prefers the midline, his arms assume symmetric positions and frequently meet above his chest. The human t.n.r. is not a stereotyped reflex, but a growing pattern changing with the maturity and the economy of the organism. It involves far-reaching elaborations in eye-hand co-ordination, prehension, prone locomotion, laterality. It displays significant individual differences in motor demeanor and psychomotor constitution.

This behavior form, which has essential counterparts in quadrupeds, exemplifies both the bonds and the cleavages between human and animal psychology. It may also suggest the validity of a broad morphological approach to the study of the human mind. In spite of an enormous descriptive literature, one might legitimately hold that human psychology is deficient in fundamental description, because it has not reckoned systematically with the form characteristics of behavior. We lack the grammar and the lexicon for formulating these form characteristics. We must develop morphographic methods which will simplify and generalize form phenomena. A psychomorphological approach will also bring us closer to the ancient problem of psychic constitution and of mental types. It is indispensable for the delineation of the ontogenesis of human behavior and the comparative psychology of life cycles.

(5) *Cultural Anthropology.* Hamlet must not be left out of the play. In fact, in the Story of the Human Mind, there are two Hamlets: the Biological Adam and Culture! Culture, as Malinowski aptly put it, is nothing but the organized behavior of man. The scientific study of the patterning of human culture would seem to constitute a fundamental approach to the science of the individual mind, which mind is in part a product, in part a creator, of the culture in which it has its being. Culture is "a large-scale molding matrix, a gigantic conditioning apparatus. In each generation it produces its type of individual. In each generation it is in turn reshaped by its carriers."

We are quoting Malinowski, for he is no mean authority and he grew up in the tradition of the exact sciences, including laboratory training in physical chemistry and experimental psychology at the University of Leipzig. As the founder of the functional school of anthropology, he holds that there exist scientific laws of culture. "Culture is a determinant of human behavior, and culture as a dynamic reality is also subject to determinism."

The term culture comprises much. It includes the prosaics of food getting and of everyday family life, as well as the exoticisms of ceremony and magic. It is not assumed that multifarious masses of anthropological data must be incorporated into the subjectmatter of psychology. However, the anthropologist sees in living cultures, in spite of their apparent diversity, a pervading sameness, arising out of common traits of human nature. This quality of sameness denotes underlying psychological laws which should enable us to better understand ourselves and our cultures, including religion, morals, mores, and government. Thus also we may arrive at more insight into the diseases of culture as manifested in poverty, economic crises, crime, and war. It is not strange that cultural anthropology claims to be the very basis of social science. But scientific anthropology, no less than psychology, is inextricably bound up with physics, chemistry, physiology, and biology. Culture began with a very primitive man who still has not lost all his primitiveness.

The understanding of the human mind, it therefore seems, will be attained not through the researches of a single discipline, but through the conjunctive results of a great interlocking system of sciences, a system which is itself the most characteristic cultural product of our technological civilization. No previous culture has ever achieved a product more magnificent than the present body of natural and engineering science. This achievement is our hope, as well as our despair. The despair will not lessen until the techniques of modern science can be more sincerely brought to bear on problems of behavior. Only through profound self-knowledge can the human mind bring itself nearer to individual and collective control.

CHAPTER V

The Method of Co-Twin Control

Growth is an irreversible process. In investigating the growth process one might like to train a child, and then compare him with what he would have been if he had not received the training. This cannot be done; there is no way to make the desired comparison. But we may study a pair of identical twins with just such comparisons in mind. We may train one twin (T) experimentally, and reserve the co-twin (C) as a control. C becomes a scientific kind of stand-in-double for T.

In 1927 the writer, in collaboration with Dr. Helen Thompson, undertook a comparative study in which two highly identical twin girls, T and C, were observed from early infancy to determine, first, their developmental correspondence and, secondly, their developmental divergence, as affected by training confined to one twin. A thoroughgoing similarity in physical and behavioral characteristics was amply established by repeated examinations and measurements.[1, 2]

The method of co-twin control had its origin in a stair-climbing and cube-behavior experiment begun when twins T and C were 46 weeks old. Twin T was trained daily in climbing a five-tread staircase. At 52 weeks she climbed the staircase in 26 seconds. Twin C, at the age of 53 weeks, without any previous training or experience, climbed the same

[1] Arnold Gesell, "The Developmental Psychology of Twins." From *A Handbook of Child Psychology*, Worcester, Mass.: Clark Univ. Press, 1931. Ed. Carl Murchison, pp. 158-203.
[2] Arnold Gesell and Helen Thompson, *Genet. Psychol. Monog.*, 6: 1-124, 1929.

staircase unaided in 45 seconds. As a comparative check, Twin C was then trained for a period of 2 weeks. At the age of 55 weeks she climbed the stairs in 10 seconds. The climbing performance of Twin C at 55 weeks was far superior to that of Twin T at 52 weeks, even though Twin T had been trained 7 weeks earlier and three times longer. At 56 weeks and again at 3 years their performance on the experimental staircase was amazingly alike. These clear-cut quantitative results, supported by minutely analyzed cinema records, established certain relationships between learning and maturity.

In a similar way for a period of 6 weeks, Twin T was trained and stimulated in exploitive play with ten one-inch red blocks. Every effort was made to perfect and to elaborate her patterns of cube behavior. Twin C again was reserved as an untrained control. Detailed analysis of cinema records showed a remarkable similarity in the cube behavior of the twins at 46, 52, 63, and 79 weeks of age.

In a later study Strayer[3] used the same co-twin control method to determine the relative efficacy of early and deferred vocabulary training. The twins were separated and kept under continuous observation. Twin T was trained from her 84th to 89th week. Twin C was trained for 4 weeks beginning with the 89th week. C reached a higher level of language performance after 28 days than did T after 35 days of training. T was only slightly superior at 93 weeks; 3 months later the difference was negligible.

When the twins were 4½ years old, Hilgard[4] used the co-twin control method to compare the effects of early and delayed practice in motor and memory performances—ring tossing, walking-board skill, digit and object memory, and paper cutting. Three months and also 6 months after practice, the performances of the twins on all tests were as similar to each other as at the beginning of the experiment.

Through an exceptionally fortunate convergence of circumstances it has been possible to follow the development of these self-same twins for 20 years. Numerous observations and coincident comparisons were

[3] L. C. Strayer, *Genet. Psychol. Monog.*, 8: 209-319, 1930.
[4] J. R. Hilgard, *Genet. Psychol. Monog.*, 14: 493-667, 1933.

made at advancing ages. Simultaneous observation with segregation of the twins was accomplished by a duplex noncommunicating suite, equipped at the end with a single one-way-vision window. The findings of these studies and of the several co-twin control experiments have been co-ordinated in a recent monograph which reviews the life careers of the twins for the whole period from early infancy to adolescence.[5] Both physical and behavioral characteristics were considered as follows: (1) *Anthropometry:* height and weight, palm prints, dentition, hair and eye color, hair histology, vision, hearing, health, eating and sleeping, puberty, homeostasis. (2) *Motor Behavior:* postural demeanors, laterality, locomotion, fine co-ordination. (3) *Adaptive Behavior:* mental growth rates, block construction, play behavior, drawing, school achievement. (4) *Language Behavior:* infant vocalizations, enunciation, vocabulary, conversation. (5) *Personal-Social Behavior:* adjustments to home and school, intertwin dominance, humor, fantasy, personality traits.

This sequential study represents a biogenetic application of the combined methods of co-twin control and coincident comparison, to determine the stability of behavior resemblances and differences. The long reach of the data, with numerous nodes for cross comparison, made it possible to analyze such factors as ontogenetic timing, physiological tempo, attentional traits, and the durability of individualities of behavior and personality. So far as Twins T and C are concerned many of our conclusions seem firmly grounded.

Some of the conclusions may be safely generalized. But the method of co-twin control has its limitations. A twin is not an absolute unit of measurement; and we must start all over again with the next pair of twins. In this sense, twins are uncalibrated and fall outside the calculus of biometrics. Nevertheless, when one reflects that even physics with its beautiful mathematical precisions is never on absolutely absolute ground, we may accord a certain pragmatic value to a method which

[5] Arnold Gesell and Helen Thompson, *Genet. Psychol. Monog.,* 24: 3-121, 1941.

applies a norm that equals in complexity the phenomena to which the norm is applied.

The distinctive feature of the method of co-twin control is its utilization of an organismic norm. Such a norm has certain advantages over a purely statistical criterion. Statistical norms and devices can never be organismic because they are either heterogeneously unselected or homogeneously selective and must therefore remain analytic and partial in application. But a control co-twin is by definition highly identical with the individual under investigation. He is in fact the sum of a statistically numerous multitude of forces. He is an embodied quantity who with respect to any distinguishable trait is more or less than the investigated individual.

A control co-twin is a synthetic standard of comparison with a highly equivalent prenatal and postnatal life career, except for divergences which are experimentally created or naturalistically observed. When one contemplates the almost infinite number of variables which enter into the shaping of any life career, it must be granted that an "identical" co-twin who brings these variables into finite and manageable range is indeed an extraordinarily powerful statistic in his own integral person. His individuality is unique, but by definition it is almost a replica of the individuality which is being assayed. The patterns of twin and co-twin do not exactly superimpose. But by matching we measure. We expose areas and directions of discrepancy. The almost complete identity of the datum and the measuring device gives augmented significance to all discrepancies which can be defined and accounted for.[6]

With such a rationale it is evident that the method of co-twin control requires that a thorough parity and identity be established by careful measurements *prior* to the period of comparative observation and experiment. If there are any significant antecedent discrepancies they should be recorded and taken into account in subsequent comparisons. H. H. Newman in an interesting chapter on the psychology of twins

[6] Arnold Gesell, *Science*, 88: 2280, 225-230, 1938.

has called attention to the importance of this aspect of the method of co-twin control. Referring to the New York twins, Johnny and Jimmie, he writes:

> One of these twins, we don't remember which and it doesn't matter, was trained to be a little gentleman and the other allowed to grow up like Topsy. As time went on they became very different in motor skills and in social behavior. This would have been an excellent case for testing the effects of different environment and training on two individuals alike in their heredity, except for one defect in the setup. Johnny and Jimmie turned out to be a pair of two-egg twins! So the co-twin control feature was entirely lacking. . . .[7]

Newman properly points out that unless one-egg twins are used it is impossible to distinguish hereditary from environmental effects. Galton had the same thought in mind, when in 1875 he wrote his famous paper entitled "The History of Twins as a Criterion of the Relative Powers of Nature and Nurture."[8]

The method of co-twin control presupposes one-egg twins of thoroughgoing similarity, with environmental factors held constant, except for precisely defined or experimentally imposed differentiations.

The method of co-twin control therefore is essentially a clinical method, designed for the intensive study of monozygotic pairs (to say nothing of monozygotic triplets, quads, or quints!). It can attain statistical status, in the ordinary sense of that term, only when a sufficiently large number of comparable co-twin control studies are accumulated. Such a statistical extension of the method was advocated in 1930 by Blakeslee and Banker in a paper entitled "Identical Twins as Biological Controls in Educational and Other Human Problems."[9] The authors suggested an endowed school for one-egg twins instructed by monozygotic twin teachers! Just at this time, Russia organized an institute for twin research in connection with the Maxim Gorky Medico-Biological Institute of Moscow. The method of co-twin control was used

[7] H. H. Newman, *Multiple Human Births. Twins, Triplets, Quadruplets and Quintuplets.* New York: Doubleday Doran. xi+214 pp., 1940.

[8] Francis Galton, *Jour. of the Anthropological Institute,* 5: 391-406, 1876.

[9] A. F. Blakeslee and H. J. Banker, *Proceedings of the American Philosophical Society,* Vol. 69, 1930.

on a systematic scale for a large variety of studies. A score of scientists pooled their resources and in 1935 some 800 pairs of twins, mostly children, had been investigated. This striking enterprise resulted in significant studies, but was terminated about three years later.[10, 11]

Although these large-scale investigations are impressive, it should be pointed out that the method is not essentially enhanced by multiplication. A large number of cases may confirm trends and define new problems; but numbers will not in themselves be productive. The method is clinical; it is productive in the single instance. It depends heavily upon the ingenuity and insight of the experimenter; and it is capable of far-reaching adaptations. The areas of possible application have scarcely been scratched. The method has numerous potentialities in the field of medicine, which already boasts a vast literature on twins and twinning phenomena. The medical literature, however, is largely documentary, rather than experimental. Co-twin control has many unrealized applications in clinical physiology, pharmacology, and experimental therapeutics.[12]

The method of co-twin control is peculiarly suited to the analytic study of the processes of child development and the genetic factors of life career. If the instincts of an organism were only tinted pink and the habits robin-egg blue, as Lloyd Morgan whimsically wished, then we might better grasp the relationships of nature and nurture, of endowment and environment. This differential stain has not been forthcoming; but with the aid of co-twin control studies we may glimpse the interrelations of learning and growth, the effects of specific training, the influence of attitudes and emotional patterns. The method may be fruitfully used to explore these intricate problems which are so resistant to absolute biometric approach. The method preserves the togetherness of the individual and affords more insight into the total integrated economy of performance and development. Critically used it is to a considerable degree self-corrective.

[10] S. G. Levit, *Character and Personality*, 3: 188-193, 1935.
[11] A. R. Luria, *ibid.*, 5: 35-47, 1936.
[12] Arnold Gesell (with Eugene Blake), *Archives of Ophthalmology*, 15: 6, 1050-1071, 1936.

When so used we come, in the end, to a better understanding not only of one individual but of two, for one reciprocally elucidates the other. When the comparisons are made successively over a long onto-genetic range, this comparative method also illumines the processes of growth. Differences and correspondences in timing establish points to reckon by. And even though the method is one of dead reckoning and lacks the elegance of classic mensuration, it may bring a mariner shrouded in shifting fogs to the vicinity of a port.

The Conditioned Reflex and the Psychiatry of Infancy[*]

I. Scientific Status of the Conditioned Reflex (C-R)

The study of the C-R has almost attained the dimensions of a sub-science. According to a recent classified bibliography by G. H. Razran[45] the C-R literature to date totals about 1500 titles of which 42.6% are Russian; 29.8% English; 13.3% German; 11% French; and 3.3% in other languages. Roughly, about 60% of the experimental papers come from European and 25% from American laboratories. The German ratio of contributions from 1933 to 1935 dropped from 15% to 5%. Do we have in these interesting statistics a cultural index of national differences in scientific outlook? It would require an international commission rather than an individual to provide an adequate critique of all this literature.

When we reflect that many of these studies represent years of research by the most exacting methods, we may well ask what import the investigations have for the practical problems of child psychiatry. Analysis of the literature reveals that only a very small proportion of the

[*] A paper presented at Ier Congrès International de Psychiatrie Infantile, Paris, July 24-28, 1937. La Section de: Psychiatrie Genèrale. From the Clinic of Child Development, Yale University.

Raised numbers refer in this chapter to Bibliography on pages 79-81.

studies address themselves to therapeutic applications. At the moment C-R concepts have had more significance for scientific theory and methodology than for psychiatry as a branch of clinical medicine.

Some would hold that the analysis of the C-R phenomena is as fundamental for psychology as Galileo's experiments with falling bodies were fundamental for physics. Others hold that the experimental constriction of C-R observation introduces such serious distortions of the normal state of the living organism that deductions are misleading if not invalid. Not without justification some of these critics say that the most illuminating results of C-R analysis consist in the explanations of its experimental limitations and inherent errors. Some experimenters, however, insist that the progressive effort to achieve laboratory control will itself lead to clarification; and that the C-R method offers a powerful tool for deriving the principles of all behavior, normal and abnormal.[18]

Pavlov's own career represents a tireless contest with the difficulties of his own experiments. He began under the spell of the scientific boldness of his teacher, Sechenov, who in his famous lecture on "The Reflexes of the Brain" in 1863 initiated a new chapter in science with words such as the following: "The child acquires consecutive reflexes in all spheres of the senses by means of absolutely involuntary learning. . . . All psychical acts without exception, if they are not complicated by elements of emotion are developed by means of reflexes. Hence all conscious movements, usually called voluntary inasmuch as they arise from these acts, are reflex in the strictest sense of the word."[47]

Historically the study of C-R phenomena cannot be detached from the broader fields of *associationism* and of *learning*. Associationism as a scientific tradition has come down from Aristotle and still has considerable vitality. The laws of association deal with the factors of contiguity, assimilation, frequency, primacy, intensity, duration, context, acquaintance, composition, and individual differences.[46] To this list must be added the pervasive factors of age or maturity, a factor of peculiar importance in the period of infancy.

The psychology of learning presents a broader front than the experimental analysis of the C-R. The study of learning has become the most absorbing and characteristic pursuit of psychologists in America. Many American psychologists would be inclined to think of conditioning as a special example or form of learning rather than as the sole foundation of a learning theory.

Knight Dunlap, however, is a realistic critic of the C-R and is unable to see in the Pavlovian physiological scheme "any vestige of explanation of learning."[9] He would insist that Pavlov has not isolated natural primal reflexes and that under the conditions of experimentation these reflexes are abnormal in character. Dodge likewise finds that even a reflex so simple as the knee jerk undergoes alteration with conditioning. He has never been able to secure under rigid experimental conditions, a conditioned knee jerk which aproached in identity its reflex prototype.[8] Few psychologists would admit that C-R experimentation has actually isolated a unit of habit. Such severe strictures on the meaning of the C-R formula place serious limitations upon the introduction of conditioning techniques into the practice of infant psychiatry.

An adequate appraisal of the scientific status of C-R theory would have to include an examination of the principles of learning. There is no agreement as to these principles. Thorndike[50] has formulated important laws of learning which coincide in part with laws of association. Meumann's[38] classic experiments with nonsense syllables have been reviewed and altered to elucidate these laws and to search for C-R mechanisms. Numberless rats have been run through numberless mazes but their experimenters have not yet threaded the labyrinth of learning concepts.

Dunlap has advanced three alternate theories of learning which are delightfully inclusive by reason of their apparent contradictoriness. He designates them the Alpha, Beta, and Gamma hypotheses respectively:

Alpha: The occurrence of a response increases the probability that when the same stimulus pattern occurs the same total response will again recur.

Beta: The occurrence of a response lessens the probability that on the recurrence of the same stimulus pattern the same response will recur.

[67]

Gamma: The occurrence of a response in itself has no effect on the probability of the recurrence of the response.[9]

Dunlap seriously believes that all of these hypotheses may hold in different cases. We shall recur to the Beta hypothesis again because it involves the principle of negative practice which stands in interesting contrast to the C-R concept.

The Concept of Maturation

Another concept which must be reckoned with in the appraisal of C-R mechanisms has its roots in the physiology of development, and has received much confirmation from the studies of experimental embryology. In America this concept goes by the name of *Maturation*. In spite of lack of precision, this term serviceably denotes the intrinsic organic factors which impart characteristic sequence and form to the ontogenesis of behavior. The operation of C-R mechanisms cannot be divorced from these underlying developmental mechanisms which determine not only somatic morphology but the morphology of behavior. Even if we should grant the validity of C-R "units," we should still have to recognize that the areas of conditionability change with age and maturity. The maturity of organisms determines the degrees and modes of susceptibility to environmental impressions.

Normative, naturalistic, and experimental studies at the Yale Clinic of Child Development have demonstrated the importance of these maturity factors.[14, 15] We have used the cinema and the method of co-twin-control to bring them into evidence. A brief example will illustrate.[13]

Twins T and C, highly identical in physical and psychological characteristics, were placed before an experimental table. Simultaneously they were presented with a small pellet 7 millimeters in diameter. At 38 weeks the twins addressed themselves to the pellet in an identical manner. The hands were placed in full pronation, the fingers were fully extended and spread apart in a fanlike manner. The thumb was extended almost at right angles. The photographic record of their attack upon the pellet in the motion picture shows an almost uncanny degree of identity in the details of postural attitude, hand attitude, approach, and mechanism of grasp.

At 40 weeks there was a crude raking attack upon the pellet; at 42 weeks this raking approach was replaced by a poking with the tip of the index finger. These changes in prehensory pattern occurred contemporaneously in both children.

At a later age (93 weeks) the twins were seated back to back, each confronting an individual experimental table. The two examiners simultaneously dropped a 7-millimeter pellet into each of two bottles, simultaneously presented. Three trials were made with each child. The examiner, having dropped the pellet into the bottle, gave the bottle to the child. Both children watched this dropping of the pellet with the same transfixed attention. Both children on the first trial, and again on the second trial, seized the bottle, apparently heedless of the contained pellet; but both children on the third trial (without of course any influence of imitation) pursued the pellet by poking at it against the glass—indicating an identical capacity to profit by experience. In this instance we find that the correspondence of behavior patternings asserts itself not only in spontaneous activities but extends into minute fields·of specific adaptation and of learning.

In such remarkable correspondences of behavior in identical twins, we see a paradigm of important relationships between conditionability and maturity. These relationships suggest that constitutional individual differences must play a powerful role in the application of methods of conditioning and reconditioning.

The concept of maturation emphasizes the unity of the organism and the priority of the total pattern of response. The unity of the organism is not conceived in mystical terms, but is identified with the functional and structural unity of the total reaction pattern. Specific patterns (learned and unlearned) differentiate out of this totality by a process of individuation and delimitation. Coghill, for example, asserts: "Conditioning of reaction, accordingly, is accompanied by restriction

[69]

(narrowing) of the zone of adequate stimulation and concomitant restriction in the field of action. The primacy of structural basis for this is in the mechanism of the total pattern."[6]

Philosophically this view may be opposed to the C-R concept which, in its classic simplicity, emphasizes the primacy of the unitary reflexes. From a C-R standpoint the behavior of the individual is a complex concatenation of unconditioned and conditioned reflexes. The totality of behavior is accordingly secondary to the constituent units. The proponents of maturational theories stress the developmental physiology of the basic total pattern.

II. Studies of Infant Behavior by the C-R Method

The first investigations of conditioned reflexes in young children were made by Krasnogorsky in 1907, using the motor reflex of opening the mouth to food. In a short summary before the International Medical Congress in 1913 he reported the establishment of conditioned responses in all normal children beyond the age of one year in from two to ten trials.

Ivanov-Smolensky used similar methods on children, both normal and abnormal. Marinesco and coworkers have since 1930 published under titles such as the following: *Hysterie et reflexes conditionnels, Nouvelles contributions à l'etude des reflexes conditionnels dans l'hysterie, Stuttering and Conditioned Reflexes,* and *Conditioned Reflex: Application to Clinical Problems, Especially Neuroses and Psychoses.*

Denisova and Figurin have conditioned infants to natural stimuli occurring within 21 to 27 days after birth; reporting that conditioning was effected in from 48 to 350 presentations of the stimulus for 15 seconds previous to and 30 seconds after feeding began. The age at first appearance of the C-R varied from 33 to 77 days. They also investigated differential conditioning in infants from 4 to 7½ months of age.

In America comparatively little work has been done on the C-R in infants. The first study was carried out by Mateer,[37] in 1918. A bandage applied to the child's eyes was made the conditioning stimulus, this being associated with the feeding of chocolate. In 1917 Watson[53] conditioned an 11-months-old infant so that he feared formerly neutral objects. The loud clang of an iron bar was brought into association with a hitherto tolerated rabbit. Subsequently the infant feared the harmless rabbit. This conditionability of emotional response was made a tenet of Behaviorism.

Ray and Wallace attempted to condition fetal kicking, using one subject. Wallace obtained negative results,[49] while Ray's results were equivocal since the neutrality of the vibrator, used as the conditioned stimulus, was not clearly established.[44] Aldrich conducted an experiment for the purpose of determining whether or not a 3-months-old infant was deaf. The ringing of a small dinner bell was accompanied by scratching with a pin on the sole of the foot.[1]

In a recent study from the Iowa Child Welfare Research Station, Wenger[55] reports an investigation of the conditioned response in infants. He finds that it is possible with perseverance to establish some form of conditioned response in some newborn infants, using standard methods (lid response conditioned to tactual vibration of the foot; withdrawal and respiratory responses conditioned to auditory stimulation). "Conditioning in the neonate is unstable and not easily obtained. These factors make it difficult if not impossible to investigate systematically many of the characteristics of conditioned responses in neonates. . . . The data contribute to the theory that internal inhibition is not a phenomenon of conditioning but an artifact resulting from an experimental environment controlled to the point of monotony."[55]

III. C-R Interpretations of Psychopathology

While working on differential conditioned reflexes, Krasnogorsky observed that his subjects tended to become irritable and hard to handle when differentiations became too difficult for them. He observed that the nicer the differentiation demanded, the more the normal balance between irritation and inhibition was disturbed. Also in forming delayed reactions he discovered that as soon as the conditions became too difficult for a subject, the balance failed and an intensive inhibition developed which increased to the degree of sleep. The disturbance of the balance was still more apparent in experimentation with abnormal children.[29]

Ivanov-Smolensky[20] explains the observations of Krasnogorsky on the basis of additional observations of neuroses experimentally produced in dogs.

1. Neurotic conduct is the expression of disturbed equilibrium between cortical stimulative and inhibitive processes: either cerebral stimulation or inhibition predominates.

2. The "psychic trauma" which is generally supposed to be the cause of the development of the neuroses from a physiological point of view is a task which is difficult for the balancing of the stimulative and inhibitive cortical processes (differentiation or integration) which task is offered to the given nervous system by the biosocial medium. . . . In the cortex a conflict of the stimulative and inhibitive processes takes place which produces an abrupt disturbance of the intracerebral balance and a widespread irradiation of the stimulation or inhibition (stimulative or inhibitive neurosis).

3. The "dislodged complex" corresponds to the originating in the cortex of an inhibitive place which is the result of an unsuccessful bio-adaptation.

4. The cause of a neurosis is the incongruity between the complicated nature of the surrounding world and the ontogenetic want of adaptability of the given cerebral hemispheres; thus that cause is the weakness of the reflex-producing, i.e., balancing capability which keeps the equilibrium of the individual and the external world by means of cortical excitation and inhibiton.

5. The treatment of a neurosis must tend not only to remove the cortical inhibition spots (dislodged complexes) but also to train the reflexogenous and balancing function of the cortex of the cerebral hemispheres.

Krasnogorsky explains neurotic behavior in similar terms. For example he believes that many tics and similar nervous disorders are merely conditioned reflexes and therefore susceptible to a conditioned-reflex treatment.

Experimental neuroses have also been produced by Liddell[2] in his studies of the conditioned motor reflexes of sheep. He transformed a docile, well-balanced animal to a stubborn, highly nervous animal, who became unmanageable for further experimentation and did not resume normal, quiet deportment in the laboratory until over a year later. Liddell found that positive conditioning led to no neurotic results but, when restraint was piled upon restraint and increasingly fine differentiations were demanded, negative conditioning strained the nervous system to the breaking point.

The striking verisimilitudes of experimentally produced neuroses have led to extensive inferences in the interpretations of psychoneurotic behavior. Pavlov even used the C-R formula to explain complicated psychoses.

C. MacFie Campbell protests that such explanation is not yet warranted. He says:[4] "There are many factors to be taken into consideration in regard to catatonia and schizophrenia and neurasthenia which make the application of the conditioned reflex formulation at present premature and inadequate. . . .

"To bring extremely elaborate bodies of doctrine into association is very stimulating, but my great difficulty is in knowing whether we may not be dealing largely with analogy which, of course, has value as it may stimulate us and make our thought a little less narrow than it has been."

Meyerson likewise says:[40] "When one studies the Pavlovian work factually, that is, independent of hypotheses, a simple reflex is modified by all kinds of environmental conditioning. No elaborate conduct is built up and it is elaborate conduct that we are interested in. In other words, Pavlov has shown us how a simple reflex act may be brought into play by all kinds of artificial stimuli, but he really shows us nothing else."

IV. THE C-R AND PSYCHOANALYSIS

Theoretical interpretations of psychopathological phenomena lead to an intriguing question: What are the relationships between C-R theory and psychoanalysis? Some writers have yielded to this intrigue and have attempted to erect a bridge from one system of thought to the other. Hull holds that it is possible to cast the C-R approach to certain psychoanalytic phenomena into the form of mathematical equations, which may ultimately realize a mathematical theory of psychoanalysis.

A few ingenious exegetes have adduced deep correspondences between the conditioned reflex and psychoanalytic mechanisms. These writers not only assume that neurotic behavior is caused by conflict between stimulating and inhibiting tendencies, but they identify the various psychoanalytic concepts as coinciding with different phases of the conditioned response. Cathectic association is likened to the conditioned response; repression (in its various forms) to external and internal inhibition; sublimation to differentiation. Adjustment to external reality is ascribed to the conditioning and differentiation processes of Pavlov; and the activating influence of the wish is derived from motor activities directed to the inhibition of the reality value of the wish. In fact, Kubie states that the analyst at work is "actually presenting a spoken version of a classic experiment on the conditioned reflex."[34]

Such an identification of C-R and psychoanalysis easily reduces to neologisms and tautology. Meyerson has properly pointed out that the fundamental Pavlovian work and the fundamental Freudian approaches are located at diametrically opposite poles. Pavlov has shown us how a simple reflex act can be brought into play by all kinds of artificial stimuli. Freud, on the other hand, shows how reflex conduct is conditioned into very elaborate behavior by an underlying unitary force of libido. In Meyerson's opinion, there is no reason for harmonizing the approach of Freud and that of Pavlov at the present time.[40]

Adolph Meyer also suggests that we are dealing with facts which should be cultivated side by side, and that one set of facts should not be substituted for another too quickly. "Let them be stimulations, each set of facts in its own way, and let us enjoy the convergence which can be observed."[39]

V. Utilization of C-R Techniques in Infant Psychiatry

In all the voluminous literature there are very few studies which deal concretely and convincingly with the application of C-R techniques in the actual solution of problems of child behavior. In a simple but suggestive investigation, Aldrich demonstrated that the diagnosis of deafness could be made at the age of 3 months by the method of the C-R. Krasnogorsky and Mateer suggest that the differential C-R methods provide procedures for discriminative diagnosis of various types of defectives and psychasthenics. In actual practice, however, such tests are conspicuously absent.

After Watson's famous experiment (in which he produced a conditioned emotional response of fear by associating the clang of an iron bar with the presentation of a toy rabbit), it was at first believed that we had in this experiment the key for unraveling behavior disorders. One reviewer (in 1930) ventured prophecy.

If Dr. Watson is anywhere right . . . the practice of psychiatry . . . in two decades will have to become nothing else than the pursuit of the art of "unconditioning." . . . He expects to see unconditioning done as reliably and perhaps as spectacularly as conditioning. . . . In the behaviorist's hands mental hygiene would consist mainly of prevention of situations in which unfavorable conditioning might be produced and of accomplishing . . . favorable pre-conditioning; while psychiatry would reduce itself mainly to following the child and rapidly unconditioning where the undesirable habit had unfortunately been produced.[42]

In spite of this Utopian outlook, the method of the C-R has been systematically used to a very slight degree. Mrs. Jones, one of Watson's coworkers, was able to uncondition the fear of the toy rabbit which Watson had produced in one of his subjects. She used common-sense procedures calculated to substitute a pleasurable association with the formerly fearful object, namely the harmless white rabbit. She associated food and mealtime with the toy rabbit until finally the child would eat willingly with the rabbit in his lap. The experiment was successful, but Jones concluded nevertheless that "a child's unlearned emotional reactions cannot be regarded as reflexes to specific and uniform stimuli, but rather they involve, in the course of individual growth, a continuous differentiation of the effective stimulus patterns."[23]

Zeuer undertook experiments to determine whether or not C-R techniques actually throw light on life situations such as are encountered in psychotherapy. His results were largely negative.[57] Similar conclusions were reached by Humphrey.[19]

Bregman, working at Columbia, reports utter failure in attempting to modify the emotional attitudes of infants by the conditioned response technique. She used wooden forms for her neutral stimuli, associating with one set the sound of an electric bell which regularly produced fear reactions; and with the other set, music, which produced responses of pleasure. When the bell and music were no longer presented, there was no differentiation between stimuli which were supposed to evoke pleasure responses and those which should evoke fear responses. Bregman concludes, "The findings call into serious question the role of conditioning as the process primarily responsible for the emotional modifications which take place in infancy."[3]

Gauger, also working at Columbia, likewise reports failure in attempting to apply C-R techniques to children. He concludes, "Teaching a child to like something is as successful when the stimulus is given alone as when it is accompanied by a satisfying stimulus. The effects of positive conditioning were not distinguishably different from those of negative adaptation."[12]

It may be argued that these negative results are due to faulty technique. But if failures occur under experimental conditions, it is evident that the techniques are scarcely ripe for ordinary application by the practicing psychiatrist.

In the practical clinical situations of psychotherapy, we deal more frequently with complicated personality problems which require reeducation or which must be approached from the broader standpoint of relearning. In its classic simplicity the C-R is fragile and variable even under optimum experimental conditions. It probably would at present prove a fragile instrument in dealing with psychotic and neurotic children.

For purposes of contrast we may refer here to the *method of negative practice* which seems to stand in such paradoxical contradiction to the C-R concept. This method has already been referred to in relation to the Beta hypothesis of learning, which holds that the occurrence of a response lessens the probability that on the recurrence of the same stimulus pattern the same response will recur. Knight Dunlap[9] has put this hypothesis to practical application in the breaking of specific bad habits including stammering, tics, masturbation, thumb sucking, and even homosexuality.

Dunlap illustrates his method by citing the case of the typist who persists in transposing *t-h-e* into *h-t-e*. Such errors are ordinarily eliminated with difficulty. He found, however, that even a small amount of practice in typing the word *in the wrong way* eliminated the error. Accordingly, in certain cases of stammering, he advises as follows: "What we are to do, therefore, is to teach the patient to stammer voluntarily, as nearly as possible in the way in which he now stammers involuntarily. Then we must cause him to practice stammering in this way, under the conditions of thought and desire appropriate to the destruction of the habit which we are using as the basis for the practice. This is simple in theory. In application it is difficult, requiring an expert psychologist for its direction; but *it seems to be effective!*"[9]

VI. Conclusions and Cautions

From this survey it is evident that the theoretical aspects of C-R investigation far outweigh technical application. There is a justification for this state of affairs. The human organism is so highly integrated that it is refractory to analytical simplification. Nevertheless, under scientific urge the quest for simplification will continue. The very difficulties of the quest will inevitably yield further data which will elucidate the complex integrity of the individual organism. In this sense C-R research, even when limited to animals, will indirectly influence the concepts and principles of infant psychiatry.

But the clinical applications must remain for some time limited in scope. Deductions from the white rat must be carried over to the human sphere with due reservations. The enigmas of human infancy demand respect both on theoretical and on practical grounds. Because of their clean-cut simplicity it will be tempting to push C-R techniques into the earliest life periods. The very primitiveness and formativeness of infant behavior invites experimental approach. But here a word of caution may be in order. It has been found that the younger the infant the more difficult it is to establish a stable conditioned reflex. In early infancy from 100 to 300 paired stimulations are required to establish a conditioned response; whereas, at the age of one year, two or three stimulations may suffice. Can we be certain that the infantile nervous system in the first stages of sensory nascency is hospitable to persistent stimulation?

There is an erroneous belief that the results of conditioning are temporary and evanescent. Recent experimental evidence reported by Wendt[53] shows that a conditioned response (the foreleg flexion to tone and light stimuli in a dog) may be retained for a period as long as $2\frac{1}{2}$ years. It is suggested that the retention was due to the fact that the dog had no opportunity to develop conflicting response systems. Such an interpretation indicates that it may be important to avoid highly artificial conditioning experiments on the human infant, because the very artificiality may result in abnormal perpetuation. An extremely artificial response in the nature of things cannot be readily replaced by responses which are natural and normal to the organism. Disuse does not necessarily lead to fading.

The maturational concept suggests that the scope of natural and wholesome conditionability is always determined by the maturity of the organism. The infant's immaturity must be considered in qualitative as well as quantitative terms, and we run a certain risk when we introduce untimely artificial stimuli repeated with artificial frequency

while the infant is in the formative phases of his sensorimotor
tion. The neonate is not even protected by the apperceptive
the 6-months-old infant, and stimuli which are apparently in...
may be nocuous to him by reason of the untilled nature of his susceptibility.

It would be ironical if the experimental analysis of the conditioned
responses of the young infant resulted in the production of abnormal
behavior rather than in an understanding of the therapeutic value of
the methods of the C-R.

There are, of course, factors of safety. The maturational mechanisms
themselves operate to make the infant immune to adverse stimulation.
His biological unreadiness safeguards him from influences utterly
foreign to his receptivity. But there must be marginal areas of receptivity where there is danger of encroaching upon his immaturity. He
then testifies to his resistance by crying, by increase of tonic immobility,
by deepened sleep, by fretfulness, by respiratory gasps, and other
forms of infantile nonconformance. Let us be duly thankful that there
are limits to his conditionability!

BIBLIOGRAPHY

1. ALDRICH, C. A. "A New Test for Hearing in the Newborn: The Conditioned Reflex."
   Amer. J. Dis. Child, 1928, 35: 36-37.
2. ANDERSON, O. D. AND LIDDELL, H. S. "Observations on Experimental Neuroses in
   Sheep." *Arch. Neurol. and Psychiat.* Aug. 1935, 34: 330-354.
3. BREGMAN, E. C. "An Attempt to Modify the Emotional Attitudes of Infants by the
   Conditioned Response Technique." *J. Genet. Psychol.* 1934, 45: 169-198.
4. CAMPBELL, C. MACFIE. See Ref. 10.
5. CHURA, ALOJZ J. "Über die Beziehungen der Bedingungs-reflexe zu der Entstehung
   der kindlichen Neuropathie." *Med. Klin.* 1932, 28: 192-193.
6. COGHILL, G. E. "The Structural Basis of the Integration of Behavior." *Proc. Nat.
   Acad. Sci.* 1930, 16: 637-643.
7. DENISOVA, M. P. AND FIGURIN, N. L. "The Problem of the First Associated Food
   Reflexes in Infants." *Voprosy Geneticheskoy Reflexologii i Pedologii Mladenchestva*
   1929, 1: 81-88.
8. DODGE. See Ref. 46.
9. DUNLAP, KNIGHT. *Habits, Their Making and Unmaking.* Liveright, Inc. New York,
   1932. Pp. x + 326.
10. FRENCH, THOMAS. "Interrelations Between Psychoanalysis and the Experimental Work
    of Pavlov." *Amer. J. Psychiat.* May 1933, 1165-1203.

*11. GACKELL, L. "An Investigation of Conditioned Inhibition in Hysterical Children." *Arch. Psychol.* 1935, 148: 52.

12. GAUGER. See Ref. 23.

13. GESELL, ARNOLD. "The Developmental Psychology of Twins." *Handbook of Child Psychology.* Ed. Carl Murchison. Worcester, Mass.: Clark Univ. Press, 1931. Pp. 158-203.

14. ———, ET AL. *An Atlas of Infant Behavior: A systematic delineation of the forms and early growth of human behavior patterns, illustrated by 3,200 action photographs.* In two volumes. New Haven: Yale Univ. Press. 1934. Pp. 922.

15. ——— AND THOMPSON, HELEN AND AMATRUDA, C. S. *Infant Behavior: Its Genesis and Growth.* New York: McGraw-Hill, 1934. Pp. 343.

*16. HAMBURGER, F. "Über Psychotherapie ein Kindesalter." *Wien Klin. Wchschr.* 1913, 64: 1313-1320.

17. HAMBURGER, F. "Über den Mechanismus psychogener Erkrankung bei Kindern." *Wien. Klin. Wchschr.* 1912, 25: 1773-1777.

18. HULL, CLARK L. *Learning: II. The factor of the conditioned reflex. Handbook of General Experimental Psychology.* Worcester, Mass.: Clark Univ. Press. 1934. Pp. 382-455.

19. HUMPHREY, GEORGE. "Is the C-R the Unit of Habit?" *J. Abnorm. and Soc. Psychol.* 1925, 20: 10-16.

20. IVANOV-SMOLENSKY, A. G. "Neurotic Behavior and Teaching of Conditioned Reflexes." *Amer. J. Psychiat.* 1927, 7: 483-488.

21. JONES, H. E. "The Retention of Conditioned Emotional Responses in Infancy." *J. Gen. Psychol.* 1930, 37: 485-498.

22. JONES, M. C. "The Elimination of Children's Fears." *J. Exper. Psychol.* 1924, 7: 382-390.

23. ———. "The Conditioning of Children's Emotions." *Handbook of Child Psychology.* Ed. Carl Murchison. Clark Univ. Press. 1931. Pp. 71-92; also 1933, pp. 271-302.

24. ———. "A Laboratory Study of Fear. The Case of Peter." *Ped. Sem.* 1924, 31: 308-315.

25. KHOZAK, L. I. "Characteristics of the C-R Functions of Difficult Children." *Psychol. Abst.* 1934, 8: 73, 697.

26. KOTLIAREVSKY, S. I. AND IVANOV-SMOLENSKY, A. G. "The Method of Investigating the Higher Nervous Activity of Normal and Abnormal Children." *Psychol. Abst.* 1935, 9: 446, 3949.

27. KRASNOGORSKY, N. I. "Über die Grundmechanismus der Arbeit der Grosshirnrinde bei Kinder." *Jarhb. Kinderheilk.* 1913, 78: 374-396.

28. ———. *On the Fundamental Mechanisms of the Cerebral Cortex in Children. Trans. 17th Internat. Cong. Med.,* London. 1931, Sect. X, Part II, 199-200.

*29. ———. "The Conditioned Reflexes and Children's Neuroses." *Amer. J. Dis. Child.* 1925, 30: 754-768.

30. ———. "Psychology and Psychopathology in Childhood as a Branch of Pediatric Investigation." *Acta Paed.* 1930, xi: 482-502.

*31. ———. "Bedingte und unbedingte reflexe im Kindesalter und ihre Bedeutung für die Klinik." *Ergebn. d. inner Med. und Kindernk.* 1931, 39: 613-730.

32. ———. "The Physiology of Cerebral Activity in Childhood as a New Subject of Pediatric Investigation." *Amer. J. Dis. Child.* 1933, 46: 473-494.

*33. ———. "Die neue Behandlung der Enuresis nocturne." *Monatsch. f. Kinderhk.* 1933, 57: 252-254.

34. KUBIE, L. S. "Relation of the Conditioned Reflex to Psychoanalytic Technique." *Arch. Neurol. et Psychiat.* 1934, 32: 1137.

35. MARINESCO, G., AND KREINDLER, A. "Des reflexes conditionnels. I. L'organization des reflexen conditionnels chez l'enfant." *J. de Psychol.* 1933, 30: 856-866.

36. ———. "Conditioned Reflex; Application to Clinical Problems. Especially Neuroses and Psychoses." *J. de Psychol. Norm. et Path.* 1934, 31: 722-791.

37. MATEER, FLORENCE. *Child Behavior, a Critical and Experimental Study of Young Children by the Method of Conditioned Reflexes.* Boston: Badger, 1918. Pp. 239.

38. MEUMANN, E. AND EBERT, E. "Ueber einige Grundfragen der Psychologie der Uebungs-phänomene im Bereiche des Gedachtnisses." *Arch. f. Ges. Psychologie* 4: 1-232.

39. MEYER, ADOLPH. See Ref. 10.

40. MEYERSON, A. See Ref. 10.

41. MORO, E. "Bedingte Reflexe bei Kindern und ihre klinische Bedeutung." *Therap. Gegenw.* 1912, 53: 151-156.

42. PARTRIDGE, G. E. Review of Watson's *Behaviorism*, 1930. *Amer. J. Psychiat.* 1932, July, 12 (1): 188.

43. PEN, R. M. "Concerning the Formation of Effective and Inhibitive Habits by Imita-tion." *Psych. Abst.* 1935, 9: 129, 1150.

44. RAY, W. S. "A Preliminary Report on a Study of Fetal Conditioning." *Child Develop.* 1932, 3: 175-177.

45. RAZRAN, G. H. S. "Conditioning: a Classified Bibliography." Long Island University. To be published in the *Psychological Review*.

46. ROBINSON, E. S. *Association Theory Today.* New York: The Century Co., 1932. Pp. 8+132.

47. SECHENOV, I. *Selected Works.* State Pub. House for Biological and Medical Literature, Moscow-Leningrad, 1935. Pp. xxxvi+489.

*48. SEHAM, M. "The Conditioned Reflex in Relation to Functional Disorders in Children." *Amer. J. Dis. Child.* 1932, 43: 163-186.

49. SONTAG, L. W. AND WALLACE, R. F. "Study of Fetal Activity: Preliminary Report of the Fels Fund." *Amer. J. Dis. Child.* 1934, 48: 1050-1057.

50. THORNDIKE, EDWARD L. *The Psychology of Learning.* New York: Columbia University Press, 1913. Pp. xi+452.

51. TRAUGOTT, N. N. "The Dynamic Irradiation and Concentration of Internal Inhibition in the Cortex of the Large Hemispheres of the Child." (Trud. Lab. Fiziol. Instit. Gertzena, 2, 177-199.) *Psychol. Abst.* 1934, 8: 273, 2406.

*52. ———. "The Effect of Difficult Extraction of Food Procuring Conditioned Reflexes Upon the General and Speech Behavior of Children." (INa. Put. Izuch. Neirodin. Reb., 316-403). *Psychol. Abst.* 1935, 9: 131, 1167.

53. WATSON, J. B. "Conditioned Emotional Reactions." *J. Exper. Psychol.* 1920, 3: 1-14.

54. WENDT, G. R. "Two and One-half Year Retention of a Conditioned Response." *Jour. Gener. Psychol.* 1937, 17: 178-180.

55. WENGER, M. A., ET AL. *Studies in Infant Behavior.* Iowa City: University of Iowa Press, 1936. Pp. 207.

*56. WOLWICK, A. B. "Materials to the Study of Conditioned Reflex Activity in Children with Weak Excitatory and Inhibitory Processes." (Medico Biol. ZH 1, 110-119.) *Arch. Psychol.* 1933, 147: 37-38.

57. ZEUER, K. "The Significance for the Problem of Learning of C-R Experiments with Adults." *Psychol. Bull.* 1934, 31: 715.

* Starred references are those which bear directly on the application of C-R techniques to problems of infant psychopathology.

CHAPTER VII

The Documentation of Infant Behavior in Relation to Cultural Anthropology*

In a normal world, science is not circumscribed by political barriers. It has only one frontier, namely the unfortified boundary between the known and unknown. On this frontier there is increasing reciprocity and interchange between related scientific disciplines. Surely the sciences of psychology and anthropology have many interests in common. One psychologist (Walter S. Hunter) has even suggested that we abandon the word psychology (with all its rarefied connotations) and substitute therefor the more substantial name *Anthroponomy*. As an "anthroponomist" one might well venture into the outskirts of anthropology.

Clark Wissler, speaking as an anthropologist, has recognized an important borderland domain: "If there is a fundamental problem in education, in psychology, in zoology, and in anthropology, it is this—*to analyze man's original biological equipment for culture, to discover its limits, and its genesis.*"[1]

How can we make this analysis without a more searching documentation of the characteristics of human infancy in its multifarious manifestations among the varied peoples of the earth? Infancy, on

* Read at the Eighth American Scientific Congress, Washington, D. C., May 14, 1940. (Proceedings, Vol. II, pp. 279-91, Department of State.)

[1] Wissler, Clark. *Man and Culture.* New York: Crowell, 1923, xi + 371.

whatever continent or island it may be found, is the pivotal center of the most pervasive of all culture complexes, the family. The newborn infant is also the focal end product of the immense, immemorial forces of biological evolution.

Maturation and Acculturation

The individual comes into his racial (and ancestral) inheritance through the processes of *maturation*. He comes into his social inheritance through processes of *acculturation*. These two processes operate and interact in close conjunction. Only through systematic studies of child development, naturalistic, biometric, and experimental, can we gain an insight into the relationship of maturation and acculturation. Here indeed is one of the most comprehensive and crucial problems of the life sciences. In this problem genetic psychology and cultural anthropology have a common stake.

The individual is a member of a species. His most fundamental behavior characteristics are those which are common to the species as a whole. Less fundamental are those which are peculiar to a breed or stock, differentiated within the species. Some patterns of behavior are so primitive that they are common to a wide range of species. The startle reflex, universal among infants and children, is also found in primates and among lower mammals in types as widely separated as bear and badger. The tonic-neck-reflex which plays such a prominent role in the early ontogenesis of infant behavior was first identified and experimentally investigated in the rabbit.[2]

Locomotion on all fours is common to man and beast, that is if we include the quadrupedal infant man. Darwin in his wide-ranging studies was equally interested in animal, savage, and civilized behavior.[3] "It seemed probable," he said, "that the habit of expressing our feel-

[2] Magnus, Rudolph. *Körperstellung*. Berlin: Julius Springer, 1924, xiii + 740.
[3] Darwin, Charles. *The Expression of Emotions in Man and Animals*. New York: Appleton, 1873, v+374.

[83]

ings by certain movements, though now rendered innate, had been in some manner gradually acquired."[4]

Infancy is, primarily, the period in which the individual realizes his racial inheritance. But infancy as a biological complex is itself a product of evolution. It was evolved not only to perpetuate a groundwork of racial inheritance but to add thereto a contingent margin of specific conditionability. Infancy whether of animals or of man is a modification of the life cycle designed to subserve the needs of individual growth. Infancy lengthens when an organism is complex. It varies greatly with different species. It varies in pattern and scope in individuals within a species. Whether the culture complex in a generation or in an aeon can alter the biological complex goes beyond the immediate question. It is more important to ascertain in what ways these two interacting complexes coincide, compete, and compromise. We return then to the basic developmental process which shapes the individual, namely maturation.

Mental maturation manifests itself in the progressive differentiation of patterns of behavior. This patterning process begins *in utero*, amazingly early. Eight weeks after conception when the fetus is only an inch in length it responds to tactile stimulation of the oral region; at 14 weeks it reacts with a patterned "sneer"; it is also able to swallow, to clasp its fingers, and to wink even though the eyelids are still fused and the wink serves no immediate practical purpose. Likewise as early as 16 weeks it makes prerespiratory movements; and at 20 weeks assumes postural attitudes comparable to the tonic-neck-reflex. In innumerable ways the fetus has already anticipated the reactions of neonatal life.

Although at this age the gestation period is but half over, the future infant is already in possession of his full quota of twelve billion neurones. Intrinsic growth processes determine the arrangement and relationships of these neurones, which in turn determine the forms and sequences of the eventual behavior. All this basic patterning, neurological and behavioral, is accomplished prior to and independent

[4] Gesell, Arnold. "Charles Darwin and Child Development." *Sci. Mon.*, 1939, *49*, 548-553.

of experience. Such patterning operates not only *in utero*, but throughout the whole postnatal cycle of mental growth. This is mental maturation.

The distinction between maturation and acculturation must not be drawn too sharply, but it must be made. Malinowski has characterized culture as "a large scale molding matrix."[5] His meaning is, of course, clear and up to a certain point incontrovertible; but in the interpretation of child development I should prefer to reserve the term matrix for the maturational mechanisms, which literally establish the basic patterns of behavior and of growth career. A matrix is that which gives form and foundation to something which is incorporated, in this instance, through growth. By growth we do not mean a mystical essence, but a physiological process of organization which is registered in the structural and functional unity of the individual. In this sense the maturational matrix is the primary determinant of child behavior.

Growth is a unifying concept which resolves the dualism of heredity and environment. Environmental factors support, inflect, and modify, but they do not generate the progressions of development. Growth as an impulsion and as a cycle of morphogenetic events is uniquely a character of the living organism. Neither physical nor cultural environment contains any architectonic arrangements like the mechanisms of growth. Culture accumulates; it does not grow. The glove goes on the hand; the hand determines the glove. And the human hand, by the way, remains a primitive survival, shockingly similar to the hand of the ancient tortoise who swam the seas and walked the earth millions of years before the advent of man.

CHARTING THE ONTOGENESIS OF BEHAVIOR

From the standpoint of cultural anthropology, mental maturation may be envisaged as that innate component of human growth which

[5] Malinowski, Bronislaw. "Culture as a Determinant of Behavior." Pp. 133-168 of Harvard Tercentenary Publication: *Factors Determining Human Behavior*, Cambridge: Harvard University Press, 1937.

tends to perpetuate the most essential and stable reaction patterns of the species. Only by identifying the fundamental uniformities of ontogenesis in infancy can we analyze "man's original biological equipment for culture."

For some years now our Clinic of Child Development at Yale University has been engaged in charting these ontogenetic sequences. We have used the motion picture camera as our research tool. The cinema is an ideal instrument for the investigation of behavior patterns because it captures the behavior in its totality; it sees the whole field of behavior with equally distributed vision. And the film remembers infallibly; it registers simultaneously the attitude of the head, trunk, arms, legs, eyes, fingers, and face. It crystallizes any given moment of behavior in its entirety. By multiplying these moments, cinematography reconstitutes the movements of a whole episode of behavior. But in the service of genetic research the cinema can also make records of succeeding days, months, or years, and bring them into seriation. Thus the cinema makes available for study (a) the behavior moment, (b) the behavior episode, and (c) the developmental cycle.

Cinemanalysis is an objective method of behavior research which enables us to approach the problems of mental growth from the standpoint of *developmental morphology*. Problems of human individuality and culture must be approached from the same standpoint.

The Photographic Research Library of our Clinic has assembled systematic cinema records of the behavior development both of normal and atypical infants. Most of the records were made at lunar-month intervals under controlled and also under naturalistic conditions. The films have been classified and catalogued by library methods and can be consulted chapter and verse.

These films have provided the source material for reconstructing the ontogenetic course of infant development. We have codified the records in *An Atlas of Infant Behavior* in two volumes illustrated with 3,200 action photographs, which delineate the forms and growth of human behavior patterns:

I. *Normative Series.* This volume portrays the growth of posture, locomotion, prehension, and adaptive behavior at lunar-month intervals from birth through 56 weeks of age. The normal infant's characteristic reactions in 25 different behavior situations are depicted in successive chronophotographs enlarged from individual cinema frames. Time values and detailed accompanying text reconstruct the behavior patterns in dynamic sequence for objective, analytic study. The infants were photographed nude to increase the scientific values of the delineations.

II. *Naturalistic Series.* This volume portrays the behavior of similar normal infants in their cultural environment under the natural conditions of domestic life: feeding, bath, play, sleep, parent-child relationships, and social situations involving other children and adults.[6]

Our subjects comprised a relatively homogeneous group from the standpoint of socio-economic status, educational background, and ancestors. The grandparents were of northern European extraction. The parents were all born in the United States of America, of middle status with respect to schooling, occupation, avocational interests, housing, and home equipment.

It is perhaps significant in this connection that a second volume seemed to us necessary to bring into relief the distinctive biogenetic variations from the developmental norms; to reveal the durability of individuality; and to indicate the multitude of cultural influences which impinge unremittingly upon the infant from the moment he is born.

The illustrations in Chapter II will provide a glimpse of the aboriginal *homo juvenis* upon whom this culture impinges. It is very apparent that he assimilates the cultural milieu only by gradual degrees; that he has vast immunities to acculturation; that his nervous system sets metes and bounds to what the societal group would do for him;

[6] Gesell, Arnold, *et al. An Atlas of Infant Behavior: a Systematic Delineation of the Forms and Early Growth of Human Behavior Patterns Illustrated by 3,200 Action Photographs,* 2 vols. New Haven: Yale University Press, 1934, 922 pp.

indeed he determines what is done. The culture is adapted to him, primarily; he adapts when he is ready.

This fundamental principle is exemplified in the development of the tonic-neck-reflex pattern (t.n.r.)—a pattern of behavior which, it will be recalled, is biologically so primitive that it appears in rabbits as well as in man. It is an asymmetric postural attitude: the head is turned to one side; the forelimb on that side is extended; the opposite forelimb is flexed and held at shoulder level.

Figs. a, b, (Chap. II), show that this attitudinal pattern is clearly evident in the spontaneous waking postures of the normal infant, whether he lies quiescent or active. Figure a shows a normal infant who at 1, 6, 8, and 12 weeks of age spontaneously and consistently exhibited a right t.n.r. Figure b pictures the same infant at 24 weeks of age. The spontaneous postural asymmetry of the earlier ages has been superseded by a symmetric attitude in which both arms flex and the hands engage above the chest at the midline. This is a lawful, developmental sequence. The t.n.r. mechanisms are not extinguished at 24 weeks; they are simply submerged by symmetric, bilateral patterns. In another month the bilateral in turn give way to new unilateral patterns: one-handed reaching, one-handed manipulation and hand-to-hand transfer, and ultimately to well-defined dextrality or sinistrality. Throughout early human development there is an almost periodic, interweaving maturation, now of symmetric and then asymmetric behavior forms, with corresponding shifts in postural manifestations.

In the t.n.r. we have an ineradicable behavior pattern which is part and parcel of aboriginal human equipment. To what extent this pattern varies for different races of men the anthropologists have not told us. If it is universal, the fact will have significance. If there are marked variations this too will have significance for the interpretation of human behavior.

Modern mothers, oversensitive to the inveterate asymmetry of the young infant, sometimes attempt to force a more symmetric attitude. As far as we know this experiment in acculturation has not been successful. As a matter of fact, the addiction of the young infant's t.n.r. postures is both a symptom and a condition of his behavior growth. The infantile t.n.r. represents a morphogenetic stage in which fundamental neurological co-ordinations are laid down to form the framework for later postural, manual, locomotor, and even psychomotor reactions such as tool using.

The t.n.r. accordingly has an ecology. Man, in spite of his bilateral construction, does not face the world on a frontal plane of symmetry. He confronts it at an angle and he makes his escapes, also, obliquely. He develops monolateral aptitudes and preferences in handedness, eyedness, footedness, and other forms of unidexterity. Perfect ambidexterity, if it exists, would seem to be almost an abnormality; because effective motor and attentional adjustments require an asymmetric focalization. The behavioral center of gravity always tends to shift to an eccentric position. Functional asymmetry also shows itself in the specialization of the radial digits, namely forefinger and thumb. Unidexterity of hand, foot, or eye does not so much represent an absolute difference in skill as a predilection for certain psychomotor orientations.[7]

Tool Behavior in Infancy

These facilitating psychomotor orientations have left their impress upon most of the tools invented by man. The spear, the hammer, the shovel, the hoe, the harpoon, the golf stick, the violin, and the rifle all reflect the developmental principle of functional asymmetry.

There are further innate neuromotor orientations which have almost literally configured the primitive implements and contraptions. When the infant is shifted from a supine to the seated position, even as early as the age of 20 weeks, he makes closing-in movements in the horizontal plane. These movements are early tokens of a brushing and scraping pattern which becomes increasingly manipulatory and exploitive. As soon as these movements, even in the contemporary infant, take on an

[7] Gesell, Arnold. "Reciprocal Interweaving in Neuro-motor Development." *Journ. Comp. Neurol.*, 1939, vol. 70, 161-180.

exploitive application we are inevitably reminded of the primitive tools for scraping and scooping.

Presently the modern infant favors a vertical orientation in his movements. This results in a repetitive banging which is charged with bygone cultural implications. Significantly enough he will bang a table surface spontaneously with his bare hand, and his banging becomes most intense and intentful as soon as his hand is implemented with an object. What was the paleolithic stone which was used for fracturing other stones but a sophisticated elaboration of this hammering response of the unsophisticated infant?

The banging of 28-weeks-old maturity appears crude. This crudeness is a function of the ontogenetic immaturity of the neuromotor system at this age. The hand is still somewhat pawlike. The digits have not become functionally specialized. But at 40 weeks the radial digits, namely the thumb and index, come into functional prominence. The American infant is under an irrepressible compulsion to poke, to pry, and to probe. He uses his index finger as though it were a tool. He uses it as an awl to thrust. He uses it as a lever to push and pry. He uses it as one leg of a pincers against the volar pad of the opposing thumb. Pincerwise he precisely plucks the end of a string and instrumentally uses the string to pull distant objects into the scope of his ceaseless manipulation.

The closing months of the first year of life constitute a period in which the elementary tool-using proclivities of the infant literally burgeon. Ceaselessly he pulls, pushes, probes, brushes, brandishes, combines, and builds. Through this poking penetration into the third dimension he discovers the physical relationships of container and contained, of bowl and handle, of cup and spoon. It is quite possible that he is retracing in a condensed manner maneuvers by which the race falteringly and accumulatively mastered the elementary physics of its environment.

(Perhaps the recapitulation concept has been too completely rejected. We do not suggest its resurrection in its original naïveté but we do suggest that the exploitational patterns of infant behavior are not whimsical or fortuitous, but are on the contrary lawful, ordered, morphogenetic phenomena, inescapable under any form of culture.)

Phylogenetic reminders appear in the constructive play and building activities of the infant. At the very beginning of the second year of life he shows a beautifully well-defined interest in seriation, reinforced by his recently attained power of voluntary release. He picks up objects one by one. He releases them one by one. At first he places them in random array, but presently under the duress of a developmental morphology he arrays the objects in vertical alignment. We put at his disposal multiple one-inch red cubes. They are his building stones. Even without a model to imitate he spontaneously arrays them in a tower. Somewhat later he arrays them horizontally in a wall. Yet later he arranges them adaptively to make a bridge. Still later, a gateway and a stairway. These are lawful morphogenetic sequences. They are inherent in the very developmental anatomy of the nervous system. Accordingly the 18-months-old infant builds a tower of three blocks. This apparently is a species norm. At the age of 3 years (for it takes another interval of 18 months) he can rearrange these three blocks to construct a bridge. It is safe to say that the elementary progressions of culture particularly in the fields of engineering have been determined by the innate architecture of the nervous system. A developmental kind of geometry is visible in the monuments of man.

Man might be defined as a being who uses cooking and eating utensils. Infrahuman primates make but meager use of tools. An anthropoid ape may use a stick to rake a banana, but does not contrive a drinking vessel. He may "learn" to use a spoon under man-made cultural conditions, but he has not so far as we know invented even a ladle out of his own imaginative resources.

The spoon is a relatively complicated tool, from the standpoint of manipulation. We have made periodic cinema records to delineate the infant's mastery of this tool. It takes considerable developmental organization before he can poise and point that lever so that it will serve as a scoop. The adaptive orientation of lever and balancing of the bowl with its burden of food depends upon neurological structures which are laid down slowly. It takes two years of growth before the higher level of manipulation is attained. The slow gradations by which the infant achieves effective control over this simple cultural implement furnish us with a suggestive glimpse into the primitive stages of evolution when man was becoming a tool user.

The prolongation of human infancy is a condition for acquiring table "manners" and eating skills. But this very prolongation entails a lengthening of formative stages of partial achievement. The motor ineptness of the infant has a deep-seated biological basis, with both a backward and a forward reference.[8]

COMPARATIVE DOCUMENTATION OF INFANT DEVELOPMENT

I have dwelt at some length on the problem of tools and utensils because man is a tool-using animal. This is a problem in which anthropologist and genetic psychologist can make common cause. The problem illustrates the fundamental importance of biological as well as ethnological approaches in the interpretation of cultural phenomena. The study of infancy proves to be an indispensable key to an understanding of the genesis of culture. The science of man requires a more systematic documentation of the characteristics of infants the world over, black, white, and brown; arctic and tropical, mountain and bush, nomadic and settled; primitive and technological; Patagonian and Park Avenue.

Perhaps we need some experimentation too—a Gilbert and Sullivan experiment in which we shall transpose two antipodal neonates, rearing the Park Avenue Infant in Patagonia, and the Patagonian on Park Avenue (not omitting perambulator, nurse, pediatrician, and nursery school!). But the study of child development is a comparative science.

[8] Gesell, Arnold, and Ilg, Frances L. *The Feeding Behavior of Infants: a Pediatric Approach to the mental hygiene of Early Life*. Philadelphia: Lippincott, 1937, ix+201.

Systematic documentation covering a wide diversity of conditions is the first essential. Orderly description comes foremost.

Extremely valuable reports of child life have been made by ethnological field workers. But much of this work has a tendency to become topical and incidental. Sometimes it has suffered from predoctrinated interpretation. The science of infancy needs downright description, factual materials, dealing with the homely realities of everyday life. Exoticisms are not so important. It is much too early to utilize theoretical preconceptions as the tools of observation. They are less harmful as devices for interpretation; but even then there is hazard because of the meagerness and selectiveness of data. Adequate documentation implies comprehensiveness and an equitable orderliness of data.

How can such documentation be achieved? We have already suggested that the cinema is a powerful instrument for recording the totalities and the contexts of human behavior. Cinematography becomes a scientific implement not when it is used merely to illustrate what an observer sees, but when it is made to supply substantive data gathered for later analysis in accordance with a systematic plan. Ideally, certain minimal essentials formulated by common agreements would be covered by all field workers concerned with family and child life. When photographic records are made in accordance with adopted procedures, the data become more comparable. And since we are dealing with the comparative aspects of human behavior, it is just this quality of comparability which should be augmented. We wish to get away from mere topicality. Even naturalistic cinematography can be channelized to increase its scientific values. It goes without saying that sound recording is essential for certain purposes and that correlated written records are necessary for adequate protocols.

We have built our argument around two co-ordinate concepts: *Maturation* and *Acculturation*. They must naturally govern the areas and the schedules of documentation. To explore the phenomena of maturation we must take careful account of chronological age, and chart in a systematic manner the maturity characteristics of advancing ages. It is also desirable to set up so far as possible simple situations which are culturally generic for the entire human species. (This is admittedly a difficult achievement, but it can be approximated.) We can get records of postural attitude, sleeping and waking, supine, prone, sitting, standing; records of locomotion, of eye and mouth movements, of prehension and manipulation, of simple problem solving, which have very general application. Only by assiduously pursuing this funda- mental biological *Urkind* and by mapping his intrinsic neuromotor equipment can we hope to draw a picture of the "natural man" who exists in the world of science, even though we shall never come upon an Emile. Such an approach is frankly normative; but all comparative science depends upon norms. And the study of infancy is potentially a comparative science. We reduce the wide-flung data to comparability in order to determine whether all races are inherently equal; and if un- equal, in what respects they are discrepant. At present we lack even the simplest generalizations concerning the universal characteristics of human development in the first five years of life.

Our second key concept is *Acculturation*. This embraces a subject so vast that adequate documentation in this field would seem to be an im- possible goal. The very magnitude of the task, however, suggests the importance of systematic and selective surveys. And again, if the methods of survey follow common standards of procedure, the data as- sume enhanced comparative value. Thrifty investments of planned documentation will yield more income than sporadic forays.

The cinema has great possibilities even here. In the documentation of the family life of primitive peoples, investigators have rather over- looked the significance of the *diurnal cycle*. The world has been spin- ning a long time. Its daily revolution has partitioned and patterned the activities of all peoples. The behavior of man is consequently sum- marized by what he typically does in the course of a single day. This is eminently true of the infant's behavior day. An accurate hour-by-hour record of a typical day, by pencil and camera, epitomizes most suc- cinctly the characteristic action patterns, the attitudes, and the infant-adult relationships which prevail. Such a record may even have quanti-tative import, when brought into comparison with equivalent records of other peoples and conditions. A typical behavior day accounts for the child's sleep, waking, cleansing, dressing, toileting, play, feeding, and a host of circumstantial ministrations and customs which if recorded with fidelity reflect the atmosphere and the morphology of a given culture complex.

I am now in danger of venturing too far into anthropological domain; but I conclude with the suggestion that such behavior-day records systematically collected would be of mutual value to anthropologists and psychologists. They would illuminate many problems of human biology. They would serve to unify the science of man by making it comparative.

Indeed, this method of *behavior-day documentation* seems so promis-ing that one would like to see it tried at home as well as in Patagonia. Right here in the United States of America we are too ignorant of the tremendous cultural differences, not to say maturational differences, which prevail among the widely varying racial stocks and socio-economic groups. To determine the possibilities of reculturating the most handi-capped areas we must know more about man's original biological equip-ment for culture. This is so fundamental that we may have to revise the famous dictum of Pope to make it read: The proper study of man-kind is human infancy. The basic likenesses and differences among peo-ples display themselves most transparently and authentically in the first years of life. These peoples may be at war or at peace. But in the uni-versal traits of infancy we still see the essential solidarity of the human race in its most genial and promising light.

CHAPTER VIII

Cinemanalysis: A Behavior Research Technique .

The pioneering photographs of a century ago depicted landscapes, still life, and sitters immobilized for portraits. Psychology as a science is interested in action, in movement, in performance. It is interested in the dynamic aspects of behavior. The 20-minute exposures required by the early daguerreotype would scarcely suffice for study of human reactions (surely not for recording the behavior of an infant who manages to do a good many things in twenty minutes!). Nevertheless, "photogenic drawing," as the daguerreotype process was called, was faster than portrait painting. It took Leonardo da Vinci four years to paint the smile of Mona Lisa.

About a hundred years ago John W. Draper, M.D., Professor of Chemistry in the University of New York, made the first sunlit portrait of the human face. He succeeded with exposures of from 20 to 90 seconds. His shade may well stir to know that it is now a commonplace to make a thousand discrete, seriated exposures in an equal length of time.

Not until photography became instantaneous did it begin to have significance for the scientific study of human behavior. Instantaneous photography freezes motion. Cinemanalysis is a method for the systematic study of such frozen sections of motion.

[96]

CINEMANALYSIS: A BEHAVIOR RESEARCH TECHNIQUE

In 1861, an ingenious inventor in Philadelphia, by name Sellars, was intrigued with the idea of capturing and reconstituting motion by means of instantaneous photography. So what did he do? He took a series of pictures of his son depicting successive stages in the act of driving a nail. He pasted each successive picture on the successive blades of a paddle wheel. He whirled the wheel and behold the boy again drove the nail into the wood!

This experiment, for such it was, foreshadowed the application of cinematography to the study of human behavior. Here was a delineation of a pattern or behavior and a potential psychological study of motor co-ordination.

Eleven years later, in 1872, Charles Darwin published his famous volume on *The Expression of Emotions in Man and Animals*. He was especially interested in crying. From London and Hamburg he had secured photographs of children in tears. He remarks: "I found photographs made by the instantaneous process the best means of observation, as allowing more deliberation."

Eduard Muybridge (in the 1870's) set up a row of twenty-four cameras to capture twenty-four consecutive phases of the motions of a galloping horse and of a running child. Edison and Eastman (in the 90's) turned the same trick with one camera and a celluloid ribbon. Thus cinematography arrived, and it is still arriving.

We may consider cinematography to be the most powerful instrument which has yet been devised for the exploration and the investigation of the motions of man—of all visible behavior for that matter, whether human or animal.

Cinematography is a refined paddle-wheel device for capturing successive phases of motion. Cinemanalysis is a method of dissecting, counting, measuring, and examining these successive phases of motion. Had the method been available to Darwin he would undoubtedly have rated it the supreme means of observation, as allowing the most complete deliberation.

Technologically Darwin was limited to single shots—to the isolated phases of a stab photography. The cinema does not stab. It records in sequence. The everyday camera records 16 phases in a single second; the speeded cinema, 32 and 64 phases. Superspeed cameras step up to 3,000 pictures per second. Ultraspeed cameras, with continuously operating film, revolving prisms, and rotating lenses, achieve from 6,000 to 40,000 and even 80,000 exposures per second.

The ultra dizzy speeds have not yet served psychological fields of research. Recently, however, Edgerton produced a record of the behavior pattern of Bobby Jones, grand slam champion, making a complete swing with a driver. The Edgerton Stroboscopic Lamp makes possible as many as six hundred separate exposures on a single plate. Such methods of magnifying durational time, and of multiplying positional space, will be increasingly applied to the minuter study of the motions of man, both for neurological and for psychological purposes.

The scientific value of cinematography as a research tool rests upon three paradoxes:

1. The cinema embalms behavior by fixating it in chemical solution, and then reanimates it in all of its original integrity.
2. The cinema captures motion by stilling it. (This harks back to the ancient sophism of Zeno who held that an arrow could not take flight, because at any given moment it was always at rest.)
3. The cinema converts past and future into a present. The flexibility of the film, and the detachability of its records, makes it possible to bring remotely separated events into juxtaposition for *immediate* observation and direct comparison. The almost magical manipulability of cinema records thus reinforces not only the visual areas but the association areas of the brain. The cinema of itself bakes us no bread. But the method of cinemanalysis opens up unlimited fields for the brain areas to operate upon.

Cinemanalysis is a research method which capitalizes the three paradoxes to which we have just alluded. The simplest device for accomplishing this analysis is an ordinary projector, mounted on a portable vertical stand, which rests on a desk or table. In the model which we have developed at our Clinic, the projector is operated by a small hand crank and throws an image 4 x 5¼ inches in size upon a white enameled plate. The operator sits at the table in comfortable and intimate relationship with the image which he controls by means of the crank.

Let us assume that the projector carries a film which has recorded the prehension of a cube (a red, one-inch block) by a 28-weeks-old infant. The operator can project the record at a normal rate of sixteen frames per second. Time and time again he can witness the selfsame behavior episode, selecting first this, then that aspect for intensive or repeated observation. By slowing the crank he can project at the rate of about two frames per second which render the behavior in slowed but confluent motion. He may project at the rate of one frame per second and get a succession of intermittent stills. He can, of course, accelerate the rate and speed up the motion. He can always slow down to regain analytic grip on the data under observation. When that grip falters, he simply reverses the crank and inspects the sequence again. If necessary, he can look at the same sequence a hundred times.

Out of the multitude of frames which are under his observational control, he can select those phases of motion which most significantly express the configuration of the behavior. If he wishes to make a permanent record of these distinctive pattern phases, he simply takes a loose leaf from his notebook, places it on the white plate, and traces the image in outline. By thus tracing a well-selected series of such outlines, he inscribes in his notebook a faithful reconstruction of the original behavior. The cinema film has an infallible memory.

This study of the forms and the transformations of behavior can be made quantitative. The film "remembers" time and distance. Each frame represents a lapsed interval of $\frac{1}{16}$ or $\frac{1}{32}$, or $\frac{1}{64}$ second, depending on the speed of the camera. Each frame is automatically registered by a counter. By reading off the counter, by measuring distances and angles, it is possible to translate the patterns of behavior into time and space values.

The detail with which any analysis is made will naturally vary with the objectives of the investigator. Elsewhere[1] we have shown that as many as 360 pattern phases can be identified in an eight-foot strip of film, consisting of 320 frames, which record 20 seconds of infant behavior. A 20-weeks-old infant closes in on a rattle, manipulates it and drops it. This behavior episode was delineated in eight selected action photographs (frames) corresponding to the entire sequence. To demonstrate the wealth of minutiae we identified individual pattern phases for head, eyes, mouth, arm, fingers, thorax, pelvis, legs, and toes. These phases fall into three categories: (a) a critical phase in which the member is at rest or undergoes a complete shift or reversal of movement; (b) a kinetic phase when the movement is under way; (c) a phase of resolution or culmination when this particular movement is completed or resolved. The grand total of phases for the foregoing episode, as stated, proved to be 360.

It is not suggested that the multiplication of analytic minutiae will in itself advance our comprehension of behavior. But it can be safely stated that there are fundamental problems of behavior form and behavior dynamics which will not be solved until we systematically penetrate those minute manifestations which are made visible only through the microscopy of cinemanalysis. We must be prepared to investigate the phenomena of human behavior with the same searching interest in structured form which the disciplines of human embryology and anatomy demand.

Cinemanalysis indeed is a kind of dissection which anatomizes the patterns of behavior. It makes the recorded reactions as tangible as tissue. The histologist who looks at a stained section of the thyroid gland through the microscope is no closer to reality than the analyzer who looks at the outlines of a behavior pattern which comes through the lens of the motion-picture projector. Both observers are dealing

[1] Gesell, A.: "Cinemanalysis: A Method of Behavior Study." *The Journal of Genetic Psychology,* 1935, *47,* 3-16.

with problems of morphology. Both observers are inspecting, analyzing, and, if need be, measuring the characteristics of form.

This, accordingly, is a morphological approach to the study of behavior. It is, if you will, an exploration of the structure of the human mind, for the organization of the human mind is faithfully reflected in the very patterns of behavior which are made visible through the chemistry and optics of cinematography.

CHARTING OF MENTAL GROWTH

There is one more fundamental but elusive feature of the mind which is captured by the cinema and clarified by cinemanalysis; namely, *growth*. The mind grows. The psychological individual is an action system—a complex system which changes with age. There is, so to speak, an embryology of the mind which embraces the whole period of growing up. Fetus, infant, and child exhibit progressively changing patterns of behavior. The subtle process which orders and organizes these transformations is mental growth.

The cinema proves to be a unique and powerful instrument for elucidating this elusive process. The forms of patterns change with maturity. We have used the cinema at the Yale Clinic of Child Development[2] to chart these form changes in systematic sequence. Beginning with birth (both premature and full term) we have made motion-picture records of characteristic behavior at monthly, and sometimes at weekly and daily intervals throughout infancy. The records being secured under standardized as well as naturalistic conditions, are comparable from age to age and child to child. We have been interested not only in how the 28-weeks-old infant grasps and manipulates a cube.

[2] A Photographic Research Library was established in 1929 to house extensive cinema records of the Clinic which embrace normative, naturalistic, experimental, and clinical studies. The records have been catalogued by library methods, and are readily accessible for demonstration and research use.

A series of sound films with explanatory commentary (by Gesell) and a new series of silent films also dealing with child development are distributed by Encyclopaedia Britannica Films, Inc., 20 North Wacker Drive, Chicago, Illinois. *The March of Time* produced a documentary film of the work of the Yale Clinic in 1946. This film is now available in the educational Forum Edition. (The March of Time, 369 Lexington Avenue, New York 17, New York.)

What did he do at 24 weeks, at 20, at 36, at 40, at 52 weeks? When does he grasp on sight? When does he oppose thumb and index finger? When does he combine cubes, build towers, build bridges?

The cinema supplies documentary evidence for a scientific answer to these questions. Cinemanalysis discloses the lines of growth which shape the maturing patterns of behavior; it reveals orderly and universal behavior trends which indicate that the growth of the human mind is governed by a physiology of development, by laws of developmental morphology. Psychological growth is a morphogenetic process. It produces changing forms of behavior which cannot be adequately studied without the aid of cinemanalysis. The manipulability of cinema records makes it possible to study such growth sequences comparatively, critically, and quantitatively.

A study of the norms and lawful trends of behavior growth is essential not only for developmental psychology, but also for clinical medicine, particularly clinical neurology and clinical pediatrics. Neurology is concerned with those deviations of behavior pattern which denote disease or defect of the nervous system. Pediatrics is concerned with all those behavior symptoms which denote illness, immaturity, or faulty development. Diagnosis and treatment in all instances depend upon an intelligent interpretation of developmental status. Whether cinema records will become clinically as routine as X-ray, we cannot yet say. Meanwhile we shall need the cinema to document, and cinemanalysis to define, the normative criteria for developmental diagnosis and developmental supervision.

CHAPTER IX

One-Way-Vision

Seeing is believing. This is the central maxim of visual education. The one-way-vision screen is a device which enables us to see many things which we could not otherwise see at all. It brings us closer to reality because it removes the distorting and the disturbing influences of the observer. It must therefore be considered not merely as a laboratory gadget, but as an adaptable technique which has many potential uses in visual education.

Our own experience with the one-way-vision screen, to be sure, began in a laboratory, in connection with the photographic-recording dome described elsewhere.[1] The dome is a hemispherical structure, 12 feet in diameter, large enough comfortably to house a crib in which an infant is placed for observation. The interior of the dome is illuminated with soft light. Cinema cameras poised on curved tracks record his behavior. Partly in order to secure ample ventilation, the dome was encased in ordinary wire netting. The interior surface of this netting was painted with several thin coats of white enamel to increase the reflection of light; but the meshes of the screen remain open to the circulating air and to the eyes of the observers posted outside of the dome. By darkening the laboratory outside, these observers are made invisible to the

[1] Gesell, Arnold, *Infancy and Human Growth*, Macmillan, New York, 1928, 418 pp.; Halverson, H. M., *American Journal of Psychology*, 1928; Gesell, Arnold, *et al.*, *An Atlas of Infant Behavior*, Yale University Press, New Haven, 1934 (2 Vols.), 922 pp.

infant within the dome. The unseen observer sees. This is one-way-vision.

The principle of the one-way screen, therefore, is relatively simple. Perhaps you have had an experience like this: You walked down a sunny path of a garden; you opened the screen door of a porch; to your surprise you found in the shadow of the porch someone whom you had not at all detected while you were in the garden. Yet this someone could see you plainly. If, for purposes of observation or visual education, you wish to secure the advantages of one-way-vision you must imitate these conditions. The observer must be in partial darkness; light should not stream directly through the screen. The observer's station should also be carpeted to "absorb" sound and light. The painted surface of the screen which faces upon the field of observation, produces a diffuse dazzle which makes the screen appear opaque. Thus the screen is transparent in one aspect only.

The valvelike action of the screen works with great effectiveness in our photographic dome. I have used the dome for purposes of clinical demonstrations for medical students. Clinical demonstrations, of course, are a form of visual education. Many a student will not believe until he is shown. Around the darkened exterior margins of the dome as many as thirty-five students may gather in amphitheatre formation. To them the dome is quite transparent. They can observe with intimacy the whole course of the clinical examination and listen to the explanatory comments. But to the demonstrator and to the infant, the students are not visibly present. I found this visual detachment so great that I was tempted to say, "Ladies and gentlemen of the radio audience!" even though this audience was scarcely more than an arm's length away!

A few hospitals have installed one-way-vision facilities to aid in the demonstration of patients. The advantages for psychiatric demonstrations, as well as for observations, are obvious. Not only does the screen create conditions otherwise unobtainable, but it tends to accentuate visual impressions. Like an etching or a miniature model, it tends to vivify the configuration of phenomena. It should be emphasized that concealment is a subsidiary or negative value of one-way-vision. It is not designed for spying, but for positive educational and scientific controls of observation.

To date, the chief use of one-way-vision has been in connection with nursery schools and preschool laboratories. We have used our equipment, not only for graduate students, but for individual parents and for large groups of students in the School of Nursing. The advantages of one-way observation for parents deserve special mention. The mother of a problem child may be so deeply and emotionally involved in her problem that she cannot see it objectively. She is invited to watch her child from the observation booth in the nursery. Here the one-way screen often works a quiet miracle. The simple intervention of the diaphanous barrier of the screen creates a new perspective, a wholesome shift toward psychological detachment and objectivity. Seeing is believing. She begins to see in a new light. This is an efficacious form of visual education and self-guidance. It reduces the necessity of verbal explanation and of exhortation. We have talked less to parents since one-way screens were installed.

The teacher in training benefits from similar forms of one-way observation. One-way screen arrangements have been successfully used for demonstrations of schoolroom activities and teaching methods at elementary grade levels. Such arrangements also have many possibilities in connection with public museums and other forms of educational exposition. Periscopes, concealed balconies, single-vision mirrors, and one-way glass all have their special uses; but the simplicity and flexibility of the one-way screen and its permeability to air, sound, and light give it peculiar advantages. Fortunately these advantages can be realized with relatively slight expenditure of funds and of ingenuity.

In conclusion, we would re-emphasize that concealment is not the sole purpose of the one-way screen. The device provides an adaptable technique which creates new psychological orientations for a clearer perception of human behavior. As such it is open to new developments in the field of visual education. One-way-vision increases the intimacy, the piquancy, and the objectivity of observation.

PART TWO
Patterns of Growth

CHAPTER X

The Predictiveness of Infant Behavior Traits*

For some thirty years the Clinic of Child Development at the Yale School of Medicine has made numerous diagnostic and follow-up examinations of the growing behavior of normal, atypical, and abnormal infants. The cumulative data and clinical experience indicate a high degree of inherent predictability in the ontogenetic sequences of the early cycle of mental growth. The data permit a few conclusions which go beyond retrospective prophecy.

The infants were examined by standardized procedures which used a clinical crib, a test table, and test objects designed to elicit characteristic responses in postural behavior (supine, prone, and upright), in prehension and manipulation, in adaptive, imitative, communicative, and social behavior. Stenographic records were abundantly supplemented by cinema records which documented the behavior patterns at progressive lunar month intervals throughout the first year of life, and at longer, periodic intervals thereafter.

The cinema records were subjected to frame-by-frame inspection and to quantitative analysis. The objective findings established general trends in the patterning of behavior of successive age groups, and

* Read in part at the Autumn Meeting of the National Academy of Sciences, Washington, D. C., November 19, 1947.

distinctive trends in the behavior patterns of individual infants. Our studies included a group of premature infants born from 8 to 12 weeks prior to full term. These "fetal-infants" showed signs of behavior individuality even during the period of their prematurity. They also manifested behavior patterns which are characteristic of a basic ground plan of growth, and which were only slightly altered by the complication of precocious birth.

The stability of this ground plan underlies the potential predictiveness of a multitude of infant behavior traits. The tonic-neck-reflex (t.n.r.) will serve as a convenient example. All of our premature infants, when lying supine, exhibited this behavior pattern spontaneously: head averted usually to the right, the right arm extended rightward: the left arm flexed toward the left shoulder, simulating a fencing attitude. This pattern is a fundamental component of the human action system. It figures in a wide variety of motor activities and stances, nonaggressive as well as aggressive. Our studies show that this behavior pattern is virtually a universal behavior trait of normal full-term infants during the first 12 weeks of life. When present in complete form it is highly predictive of the following sequence of ontogenetic events:

(1) at 16 to 20 weeks the infant's head will prefer a midposition; the asymmetric attitude is superseded by the symmetro-tonic-reflex (s.t.r.); as he lies in the crib both arms will flex and the hands will engage above the chest. We may further predict they will indulge in mutual fingering!

(2) at 24 weeks (in a supported sitting position) the infant will seize an object of interest on sight with bilateral approach.

(3) at 28 weeks he will seize it unilaterally with a palmar grasp, and transfer it from hand to hand.

(4) at 40 weeks he will seize it with digital grasp and with thumb opposition.

(5) at 80 weeks he will prehend and manipulate with considerable interchangeability of hands.

(6) at about the age of 2 years and again at 4 years he will show a preferred use of his dominant hand.

The foregoing age assignments are approximate. The sequence, however, is highly similar from child to child, and has both practical and theoretical implications for the concept of predictiveness.[1]

There are two major types of the t.n.r., a right and a left. So a more specific question arises: Does a right t.n.r. predict right-handedness and a left t.n.r. left-handedness? On nineteen cases we have reliable cinematic and other evidence as to the dominance of the t.n.r. and of the subsequent handedness at 1, 5, and 10 years. In fourteen out of nineteen cases the t.n.r. was definitely predictive; four cases were consistently left handed throughout; the remaining five cases were ambiguous, variable, or contradictive. Clinical observation confirms these trends. An infant strongly addicted to a left t.n.r. in the first 12 weeks of life is by nature left handed. We might also predict that unwise interference with this propensity will produce difficulties, both for the organism and the culture.

One more specific question arises. Suppose that the tonic-neck-reflex is not superseded by the symmetro-tonic-neck reflex at 20 weeks, but continues to dominate the behavior picture at 28 weeks and later. This signifies a neuropathological condition and predicts that the child

[1] The significance of the concept of predictiveness in developmental diagnosis was recently illustrated in a clinical demonstration arranged for a group of medical students. Through a physician we had learned of an infant boy who was born April 28, 1947, but whose expected birth on the basis of menstrual history had been scheduled for June 1. The premature birth occurred without any premonitory or obvious complications. The child had a birth weight of 1900 grams (circa 2 pounds). His chronological age at the time that he came to our attention was 25 weeks. On the basis of birth weight we assumed the child to be from 5 to 7 weeks premature; the corrected chronological age was reckoned to be from 18 to 20 weeks.

We had not seen the child prior to the clinical demonstration. On the assumption that there were no concealed complications, we predicted that the child on examination would probably show residuals of a tonic-neck-reflex with a predominance of symmetro-tonic patterns, closing in reactions on a dangling object, and a spontaneous mutual fingering type of play. Less confidently, we predicted that the head station would be erect but show some unsteadiness. We also anticipated that confronting a table top with a test object, he would scratch in the vicinity of the object rather than reach for it directly on sight.

The child did not disappoint us. The prematurity had produced no traumatic aftereffects. The foregoing "predictions" were fulfilled. In the afternoon we examined a full-term child, born out of wedlock, with a chronological age of 20 weeks. The behavior patterns of these two infants showed a high degree of similarity with respect to their maturity characteristics.

[111]

will never be able to walk, even though he may be relatively intelligent in his adaptive behavior.

There is a vast amount still to be learned about the normal ground plan of the t.n.r. and its individual variations with reference to unilaterality, monocularity, binocularity, eyedness, footedness, eye movements, and eye-hand co-ordinations, and individual difference in visual attention patterns. The investigation problems are inexhaustible. And refinement of knowledge will eventually lead to refinement of predictions.

When we take the supine infant and place him on his abdomen he discloses more of his repertoire of behavior patterns. They are interesting because they represent ontogenetic stages in the transitions from quadrupedal to bipedal postures. Our studies have identified over twenty such stages, from the passive kneel of the neonate through pivoting, crawling, creeping, and plantigrade progression. Although there are many individual variations, there also are consistent trends. If at about the age of 28 weeks, the infant presses the inner side of one foot against the supporting surface, thus approaching a stepping position, it is highly probable that he will later assume a plantigrade stance and progress on palms and soles (Ames).

But here it is well to point out the fallibility of prediction, particularly when unusual cultural or environmental stresses are brought to bear on the growing organism. Infant L.D. came under our observation at the age of 32 weeks. He was a normal infant, but inherited a very long and large head which caused the parents undue concern. To lend support to the head and to avoid asymmetry that might come from a lateral head posture, the parents contrived a firm hollowed-out pillow. As a result the infant never assumed the normal lateral head position of the t.n.r. The growth forces were so distorted by this unnatural circumstance that the hitherto unpredictable happened. Placed supine he arched his back in pronounced opisthotonos, set the soles of the feet, his hands, and the crown of his head in locomotor stance and hummocked across the floor. Although this aberrant behavior was not foreseen, he still remained within the realm of predictability. Placed in prone position he pivoted in a very acceptable manner, normative for his age. Other stages of prone behavior followed in ordinary sequence. The course of behavior development is well ballasted by maturational determiners—the net effect of gene factors.

The power of these gene factors is demonstrated by the remarkable behavioral correspondence exhibited by identical monozygotic twins. We have intensively followed the developmental career of one pair of such twins from early infancy to maturity. Applying the method of co-twin control, Twin T was used as a measure of her twin sister, Twin C, to determine the permanence of native similarities and of induced and native differences. Since infancy these twins have followed amazingly parallel careers and have remained throughout almost indistinguishable. On the basis of detailed cinema records and of extensive periodic clinical and experimental observations, it has been possible to establish a constellation of small but consistent behavior differences dating from infancy and persisting through childhood and adolescence. Twin T is slightly quicker in movement, more direct, more decisive. Twin C is more deliberate, more relaxed, somewhat more sociable. Twin T tends to be more angular in her movements as registered in postural demeanor, in gait, and in dancing. Twin C has displayed an equally consistent tendency toward curvedness. This is objectively recorded in their drawings as follows: Twin T draws a straight mouth, attaches a straight string to her balloon, hangs triangular curtains in her house, attaches a straight pull cord, and the chimney of the house emits streaming smoke. C, in contrast, draws a curved mouth, attaches a curving string to a balloon, hangs flounced curtains, and attaches a curved pull cord hook, her chimney emits curling smoke. Twelve years later when the twins were 20 years of age, we asked them again to draw a house with smoke coming out of the chimney. True to form Twin T drew straight line smoke, Twin C curving smoke. Twin T is more definitely right handed and shows more postural asymmetry while writing and drawing.

[113]

Differences in attentional patterns were repeatedly revealed in impersonal problem-solving situations and in social situations as indicated in the following comparative table.

ATTENTIONAL CHARACTERISTICS

Twin T	Twin C
Prompt initial pick up	More deliberate initial pick up
Intense fixation	More relaxed fixation
Sharp focalization	More diffuse focalization
Decisive	Roving
Discrete	Confluent
Delimited	More sensitive to context and margins
Selective for details	More comprehensive and extensive
More varied adaptive exploitation	More imaginative personal-social elaboration
Specifically alert	More generally alert
Less initiative in social situations	More initiative in social situations

All these differences are small in magnitude and could not be stated except in terms of co-twin comparison. An extremely similar co-twin constitutes an effective measuring device which delimits a host of variables, and confers a special kind of statistical validity upon the comparative findings. The differences noted are slight but they are so deep seated that they were foreshadowed in infancy. By means of cinemanalysis it has been possible to make a comparative study of the behavior patterns which had been extensively recorded while the twins were still infants. The predictions were not made, but they were present in latent form twenty years ago.

We draw from this study the conclusion that with more adequate technique it will be possible to ascertain numerous infant behavior traits which have predictive import, because they reveal the psychic constitution of the individual. The method of cinemanalysis has already demonstrated that the child of 5 and 10 years of age tends to remain true to psychomotor constants of tempo, rate, and pattern which he displays during the first year of life.

Apart from cinemanalysis there are almost no biometric devices for the early recording and identifying of complex psychic-constitutional traits. In the appraisal of these traits, much use must be made of clinical methods and normative criteria of development. But this does not subtract from the essential predictiveness of infant behavior traits. Even with our present diagnostic tools, the possibilities of constructive clinical prediction are enormous.

Skillful clinical judgment sets its own limits of prediction and adapts them to the consistency of the available data. Clinical judgment is, of course, subject to grave errors and pitfalls, but clinical method should not be set in contradistinction to scientific method nor to mensuration. Even exact mathematical determinations need the qualification of critical (clinical) judgment based on experiential familiarity with the total complexity of the problem in question. Accordingly, a single systematic examination of infant behavior frequently suffices to establish a diagnosis and a reliable forecast of the approximate trends and limits of a developmental career. In obscure cases the prognosis must be built up through successive examinations which lead to increasing precision. The very complexity of the growth process is offset by a stabilizing integrating factor which creates opportunities for diagnosis and prognostication.

By methods of developmental diagnosis supplemented with clinical experience, it is possible to diagnose in the first year of life nearly all cases of amentia, of cerebral injury, many sensory and motor defects, and severe personality deviations. One or two examinations in infancy usually suffice to determine whether a child is suitable for adoption and whether the developmental outlook is favorable, highly favorable, or unfavorable. Examination in infancy and observation during the preschool years can reveal various forms of giftedness, temperamental qualities, individual modes of growth and learning, liabilities and assets in emotional equipment, and a host of specific trends in personal-social conduct and parent-child relationships. All these possibilities in the realm of prediction have been demonstrated by clinical applications which operate with significant success when based on a precise knowledge of the developmental mechanisms involved.

The task of science is to increase such knowledge and to make it more usable through objective diagnostic methods and biometric techniques. Mental growth is an orderly process governed by profound laws of morphogenesis. Growth phenomena, therefore, are in essence predictable. Accepting this premise, the period of early infancy becomes of basic importance for preventive medicine and other forms of social control.

BIBLIOGRAPHY

AMES, LOUISE BATES. "Precursor Signs of Plantigrade Progression in the Human Infant." *J. Genet. Psychol.*, 1939, 55: 439-442.

GESELL, ARNOLD. "The Tonic Neck Reflex in the Human Infant: Its Morphogenetic and Clinical Significance." *J. Ped.*, October 1938, 455-464.

———. "Early Evidences of Individuality in the Human Infant." *Scientific Monthly*, September 1937, 217-225.

GESELL, ARNOLD (in *collaboration with* CATHERINE S. AMATRUDA). *The Embryology of Behavior: The Beginnings of the Human Mind.* New York: Harper, 1945, xix-287.

GESELL, ARNOLD AND AMES, LOUISE B. "The Ontogenetic Organization of Prone Behavior in Human Infancy." *J. Genet. Psychol.*, 1940, 56: 247-263.

———. "The Development of Handedness." *Ibid.*, 1947, 70: 155-175.

GESELL, ARNOLD AND THOMPSON, HELEN. "Twins T and C from Infancy to Adolescence. A Biogenetic Study of Individual Differences by the Method of Co-Twin Control." *Genet. Psychol. Mono.*, 1941, 24: 3-121.

GESELL, ARNOLD, THOMPSON, HELEN, AND AMATRUDA, CATHERINE S. *Infant Behavior: Its Genesis and Growth.* New York: McGraw-Hill, 1934, viii+343.

GESELL, ARNOLD ET AL. *Biographies of Child Development: The Mental Growth Careers of 84 Infants and Children.* A Ten Year Study from The Clinic of Child Development at Yale University. Part I by Arnold Gesell: Part II by Catherine S. Amatruda, Burton M. Castner, and Helen Thompson, New York: Hoeber, 1938, xvii+312.

CHAPTER XI

Some Observations of Developmental Stability*

Dodge has emphasized the ubiquitousness of human variability and by his searching methods he has illumined the nature and significance of this variability. When we use the term *stability*, we do not call into question the phenomena of variability, but we indicate that they are themselves variable and occur in various degrees and in diverse contexts. As Dodge himself has suggested, "The scientific question is not the existence of variability, but how much, under what conditions, and with what consequences."[4]

An examination of some of the evidences of human stability may serve a purpose here. I shall presently offer some observations which illustrate the restricted limits within which variability frequently operates.

PHYSIOLOGICAL STABILITY AND VARIABILITY

Whether biometrically or teleologically regarded, variability is a relative concept, inevitably correlated with a principle of stability. In all dynamic phenomena there are pervasive factors which lead to stability.

* A contribution to the Commemorative Volume in honor of Professor Raymond Dodge, February 20, 1936. Psychological Monographs Volume 47, Whole No. 212.
Raised numbers refer in this chapter to Bibliography on pages 125-126.

The tendency to stability characterizes inorganic as well as organic systems. In one of his essays on "The Order of Nature," L. J. Henderson remarks pithily, "The stability of environmental conditions is necessary to the duration of systems."[9] This statement is, in a sense, equally applicable to the surface of the earth, to the properties of the ocean, to the fluid matrix of the body, and even to complicated dynamic systems with which biology (and psychology) are concerned. Environmental conditions may be internal or external. They may be intimate or remote. They are so numerous, complicated, and interactive that it is difficult to draw a sharp line between endogenous and exogenous influences. The net result of this interaction reveals itself as a tendency to stability which sets metes and bounds to variability.

It does not follow that there is a universal antagonism between stability and variability. On the contrary, relative stability in certain "systems" within the organism may favor the manifestation of adaptive variability in other systems. Claude Bernard's famous dictum, *"La fixité du milieu intérieur est la condition de la vie libre,"* suggests this very connection. J. Barcroft believes that Bernard's principle is as thoroughly established as any in modern physiology and adduces illustrations which have more than analogical pertinence for psychological problems.

Take hydrogen-ion concentration, for example. In spite of every opportunity to the contrary, it remains in man remarkably constant. The variation is roughly from 1 to 5 gms. in 10^8 liters, "equivalent to 1–5 gm. of hydrogen spread over the total volume of plasma of all the people in the United Kingdom or about half the people in the United States." Yet that is the variation for the extreme limits of human life, the variation as between fatal coma and fatal convulsions.[1]

Regulation in the organism is, according to Cannon,[2,3] the central problem of physiology. As such it touches the psychological aspects of variability at many points. The central nervous system on the one hand governs the stability of the internal environment, and it is the nervous system which peculiarly suffers when the limiting concentrations of hydrogen, oxygen, glucose, water, sodium, and calcium, etc., are transgressed. Deficiency of glucose, for example, results in "nervousness," a feeling of goneness, hunger; deficiency of calcium, in nervous twitchings. Excessive water engenders headache, nausea, dizziness, asthenia, inco-ordination. Excessive sodium produces reflex irritability, weakness, paresis. "The fixity of the internal environment," Barcroft concludes, "is in short the condition of mental activity." "The highest functions of the nervous system demand a quite special constancy in the composition of its intimate environment." This environment includes the cerebrospinal fluid which has been characterized as a protein-free filtrate in equilibrium with the plasma.

Many of the ephemeral variabilities of human functioning may be due to fluctuations or inconstancies of internal milieu. On the other hand, advanced forms of adaptive variability may be dependent upon a highly stable milieu and a consolidated developmental organization. Productive modifiability implies stability as well as a certain degree of instability. Stability and variability coexist not as contradictory opposites, but as mutual complements. The relationships are extremely complicated and specific. They may be studied in a dynamic aspect in narrow fields restricted to small periods of duration. They may be studied in a developmental aspect against the broader time frame of the ontogenetic cycle. Although we would not make a fundamental distinction between dynamic and developmental mechanisms, we shall here consider the latter for any perspective they may give to the general problem.

The Stable Aspect of Growth

Growth is a process of progressive differentiation and organization which leads to specific ends. To a considerable extent these ends are inherent in the organism. Growth displays a prodigious capacity to adapt to adversities and exigencies of extrinsic origin. In this sense the growth of any individual is plastic, labile, variable. But it retains durable characteristicness and this is its stable aspect. Every child has a distinctive growth pattern established in large measure prior to birth and in infancy.

Distinctive growth patterns are often most apparent in mentally defective individuals. I have had opportunity to observe the growth careers of special cases over a period of years. *C.E.* first came under my observation at the age of 13 years and has now been followed for 20 years.[7] Physical and mental measurements made at intervals show a marked consistency in his development during adolescence and an equally striking constancy in his adult years. In the first 7 years, maintaining an even ratio of advance, he rose from a mental level of 4½ years to one of 5½ years; from the latter level he has scarcely deviated even in minor details for over a decade. Still more significant is the persistence of his physical asymmetry. He was born with a total unilateral hypertrophy, which on successive measurements, has shown no amelioration or readjustment during all these years. Here is an instructive instance of the tenacity of certain growth errors. The hemihypertrophy probably arose out of a slight imbalance in the twinning process of an early embryonic stage. Yet this imbalance is projecting itself immutably throughout the life cycle—an amazing even if perverse stability.

Another impressive instance of stability recently presented itself in *O.C.*, a cretin, age 44 years, whom I first examined 24 years ago when he was a "pupil" in a special class for defective school children. On this examination his behavior level was approximately 6 years. After 24 years his behavior level remains the same. On numerous tests of judgment, drawing, hand writing, memory span, counting, and comprehension, he shows almost unaltered the behavior patterns which he exhibited when he was just out of his teens.

As sample evidence of this persistency of patterns, compare two pencil drawings of a man without copy, one made in 1911, the other in 1935. These drawings are objective records which contain useful data. (See Chapter II.)

First, what are the differences in these two drawings—differences which betray the irrepressible manifestation of human variability? The 1911 drawing is larger and bolder. Its perpendicular scope is 4¼ inches as opposed to 3⅝ inches in 1935. This contraction of ⅝ of an inch is in some way associated with maturity factors. The patient himself was 48 inches tall in 1911, and has undergone a slight shrinkage!

The lines of the early adult drawing are more fluent, more curving, more uniform, and lighter in pressure value. With proper instrumentation these differences could be given quantitative expression, but they are unmistakable in the original drawings.

The late drawing shows more sophistication; the ear is more configured; hair has made its appearance behind and above the ears, a hand is portrayed at the wrist, the eye is more orbicular, the opacity of the arm is recognized and the primitive transparency of the younger drawing is removed.

In spite of these anatomical improvements, the early drawing is aesthetically more satisfying. It has more verve, and movement. The cap has a vital tilt and the drawing has not suffered from effects of auto-criticism. In comparison, the older drawing is harder and more settled. But giving due weight to these differences, the drawings certify to a remarkable stability in this reaction system over almost a quarter of a century.

The relative simplicity of cretin psychology has helped to bring this stability into relief. There can be no doubt that the internal milieu of the cretin maintains a high degree of constancy which favors the integrity of his mental processes. This patient (*O.C.*) had no thyroid during childhood. Experimentally at the age of 38 years a grain a day was administered. On this treatment he lost weight, became irritable and somewhat difficult to manage even in an institution. Here we have another reminder of the importance of the fixity of the internal environment.

Another case of hypothyroidism in a girl, 27 *M*, has been periodically studied at our Clinic* since early infancy.[7] This child was 27 weeks of

* Dr. Ethel C. Dunham has kindly made available to me her early case records. Periodic developmental examinations were made by Miss Elizabeth E. Lord and Mr. Burton M. Castner.

age when she was first referred to us for examination. Thyroid treatment was immediately initiated and has continued ever since. During the course of 10 years we have made 26 successive determinations of behavior status. The resultant graph summarizes the course both of physical and mental growth under thyroid therapy (Chapter II).

Sixteen developmental examinations were made between the ages of 6 and 33 months. There was a precipitous rise in the weight curve and a steady rise in the height curve. At 18 months both height and weight curves were well above the normal. The mental-growth curve, plotted on the basis of behavior maturity, showed a dramatic spurt from a 1-month level at 6 months, to a 4-month level at 9 months, and a 15-month level at 18 months. The 15 to 18 ratio represents a developmental quotient (D.Q.) of 80.

Over a period of nearly ten years this child has remained remarkably true to this quotient. She has a modest, but normal, intelligence which is undergoing consistent growth, thanks to the thyroid. She has consumed over 1½ troy pounds of thyroxin in ten years. This biochemical is essential for maintaining the metabolic integrity of the body-fluid matrix; it is equally essential for maintaining the morphogenetic metabolism which underlies the life cycle.

THE STABILIZATION OF LIFE CYCLE

Medical and psychological literature are now replete with instances of detailed resemblance in both normal and abnormal twin pairs. Elsewhere we have discussed the developmental correspondence in the physical and mental traits of Twins A and B,[5, 6] and Twins T and C.[8] The remarkable similarities of the gifted twin children A and B have continued into their adult years. The correspondences of the infant twins T and C, likewise, have been maintained to an impressive degree during the past seven years, and confirm the existence of strong stabilizing factors in the mechanism of development.

Such factors are fundamentally of a biochemical nature. Just as homeostatic arrangements maintain the steadiness of the current states of the organism, so comparable arrangements within the organism normally insure a steady consistency of progression of its life cycle. In highly identical twins we see emphasized what happens with any ordinary individual. Even in infancy the individual exhibits a characteristicness of behavior reactions and of growth trends. This characteristicness continuing from month to month and from year to year must be based upon chemical (or neurochemical) mechanisms which constantly prevent the individual from becoming somebody else! The fact that three tomes have already been assembled on Chemical Embryology[10] suggests that someday we may know more concretely how these idiomatic, stabilizing regulations operate.

The similarity of reaction of identical twins to biochemical tests is a fact with vast implications for developmental psychology. It betrays the presence of deep-seated chemical factors which control not only the matrix of body fluids, but also the ontogenetic mechanisms of individual constitution. Among these biochemical tests we include not only blood agglutination and metabolic tests, but reactions to vaccine and to infections; allergy determinations, and disease susceptibilities. The pathology of twins supplies overwhelming evidence of the existence of individual biochemical or physiological traits which in principle have a far-reaching significance for the science of behavior.

In order to demonstrate more convincingly the presence of such biochemical identities in Twins T and C, I have made a more detailed analysis of their reactions to an apparently simultaneous infection at the age of 19 weeks. On November 2nd both children were vaccinated on the thigh. A week later they began to have several green watery stools daily. On the 13th the condition of the children simultaneously became acutely worse, with symptoms of drowsiness, ashen pallor, sunken eyes, and extreme dehydration. They were admitted to a hospital with a diagnosis of acute intestinal intoxication. A total of 400 c.c. saline was given immediately subcutaneously and intraperitoneally. Intravenous glucose was given at the same sitting, 65 c.c. to Twin T and 75 c.c. to

Twin C. The following day 300 c.c. saline was given subcutaneously and on the 15th of November, 250 c.c. of saline was given subcutaneously. The symptoms cleared and the sudden improvement in appearance of both twins was little less than remarkable. Their course of convalescence was similar with one exception presently to be noted.

TABLE I

TEMPERATURES OF TWINS T AND C (AGE 18-21 WKS.)

The table lists the highest and lowest temperature recorded each day, the range of temperature for each day, and the difference in range for T and C.

Nov.	T				C			T-C Diff.
	L	H	Diff.		L	H	Diff.	
8		37.78				37.66		.12
9		38.22				39.33		—1.11
11		37.0				37.78		—.78
12		38.33				38.89		—.56
13		38.0	0.		38.5	39.0	.5	—.5
14	38.0	39.0	1.		36.2	39.4	3.2	—2.2
15	36.6	38.2	1.6		36.4	39.2	2.8	—1.2
16	36.2	37.4	1.2		36.4	37.4	1.0	.2
17	36.8	37.2	.4		37.0	37.4	.4	0.
18	37.0	37.6	.6		37.0	37.4	.4	.2
19	36.5	37.2	.7		36.4	37.4	1.0	—.3
20	37.0	37.6	.6		36.8	37.6	.8	—.2
21	36.8	37.8	1.0		36.8	37.8	1.0	0.0
22	37.0	37.2	.2		36.8	37.4	.6	—.4
23	36.8	37.6	.8		36.6	37.4	.8	0.
24	37.0	37.4	.4		37.0	37.6	.6	—.2
25	36.8	37.6	.8		37.0	38.4	1.4	—.6
26	37.0	37.4	.4		37.4	38.2	.8	—.4
27	36.8	37.4	.6		37.0	37.4	.4	.2
28	37.0	37.6	.6		37.0	37.8	.8	—.2

Physical examination on admission to the hospital showed both vaccination lesions to be in a similar encrusting stage. The children were highly comparable. Twin C's temperature on admission was somewhat higher than Twin T's. Twin T's pharynx was clear; Twin C's was slightly injected, her nose showed an old discharge, and her eardrums a margin of reddening. This condition culminated in a frank bilateral otitis media of the suppurative type in Twin C on the 25th of November, associated with a slight loss of weight and with a sharp rise of temperature. The temperature subsided on treatment.

SOME OBSERVATIONS OF DEVELOPMENTAL STABILITY

Since temperature regulation is an important homeostatic function, the subjoined comparative table of temperature readings becomes of some interest (Table 1). This table indicates the highest and lowest temperature record each day, the daily range of temperature, and the difference in range for T as compared with C. Twenty such determinations were made for 20 successive days. Seventeen readings show variations of less than 1°; 3 daily readings show no daily variations at all; 11 show variations of ½° or less. All of these discrepancies are in favor of Twin T who escaped the complications of acute otitis media. The remarkable similarity in the temperature readings for the twins is illustrated in the comparative mirror chart. (Chapter II.)

The weight charts for the two children during the period of their illness show an equally impressive trend toward similarity. (Chapter II.) Even under the stress of an extremely threatening infection and under the strain of its heroic treatment, the twins made similar weight gains. On two days, namely the 22nd and the 23rd, they weighed exactly alike! Such astounding indications of metabolic parity signify the presence of deep-seated biochemical correspondences which in these twins have projected themselves on an extensive scale into the details configurations of behavior pattern.

These correspondences in behavior pattern testify to stabilizing mechanisms which control the cycle of mental growth. Mental growth is both labile and stabile. But nature sets metes and bounds to the lability. Variability is constantly channelized. Homeostasis safeguards the integrity of the individual on the so-called physiological level. Closely related mechanisms of maturation give integrity to the life career. This is the stable aspect of growth.

BIBLIOGRAPHY

1. BARCROFT, J. *Features in the Architecture of Physiological Function.* New York: Macmillan, 1934. Pp. 368.
2. CANNON, W. B. "Organization for Physiological Homeostasis." *Physiol.* Rev., 1929, 9, 3, 399-431.
3. ———. *The Wisdom of the Body.* New York: W. W. Norton, 1932. Pp. 312.

4. DODGE, R. *Conditions and Consequences of Human Variability.* New Haven: Yale University Press, 1931. Pp. 162.

5. GESELL, A. "Mental and Physical Correspondence in Twins." *Scient. Mo.,* 1921, 14, 4-5, 305-344.

6. ———. *The Mental Growth of the Preschool Child.* (A psychological outline of normal development from birth to the sixth year, including a system of developmental diagnosis.) New York: Macmillan, 1925. Pp. 447.

7. ———. *Infancy and Human Growth.* New York: Macmillan, 1928. Pp. 418.

8. GESELL A., AND THOMPSON, H. "Learning and Growth in Identical Infant Twins. An Experimental Study by the Method of Co-twin Control." *Genet. Psychol. Monog.,* 1929, 6, 1-123.

9. HENDERSON, L. J. *The Order of Nature.* Cambridge: Harvard University Press, 1925. Pp. 234.

10. NEEDHAM, JOSEPH. *Chemical Embryology.* Cambridge (England): University Press. New York: Macmillan (Distributors), 1931. Pp. 2021.

CHAPTER XII

Early Evidences of Individuality

There is a popular impression that all babies are much alike, especially young babies. This impression has received some scientific support from those psychologists who hold that the behavior of infants is chiefly patterned through conditioning processes and through specific learning. On the basis of the conditioning theory of development, individual differences at birth are slight and increase with age.

Without pressing unduly the old issue of nature versus nurture, we may profitably investigate the question whether individual differences do or do not declare themselves early in life. At the Yale Clinic of Child Development we have gathered data on the problem by periodic behavior surveys of normal infants, by clinical studies of defective and atypical infants, by comparative studies of infant twins, by biographic records of the feeding behavior of infants, and by naturalistic cinema records of infants in the situations of everyday life.

The present report is based upon an analysis of the cinema records of five normal infants from homes with high-average living conditions (Girl A, Girl B, Boy A, Boy B, Boy D, as delineated in *An Atlas of Infant Behavior*[1]). These children were photographed under homelike conditions at lunar months throughout most of the first year. Extensive

[1] Gesell *et al.*: *An Atlas of Infant Behavior: A systematic delineation of the forms and early growth of human behavior patterns.* Illustrated by 3,200 action photographs, in two volumes. New Haven: Yale University Press, 1934. Pp. 922.

cinema records embraced the major events of the infant's day, namely sleep, waking, bath, dressing and undressing, feeding, play, and social behavior at advancing age levels. Briefer cinema records and psychological observations of the same children were made at the age of 5 years.

A trained and unbiased observer, Mrs. Louise B. Ames, who had never seen the infants and who knew nothing about them, undertook a detailed analysis of the cinema records covering the first year of life. She made a summary of the behavior of each infant, at each month; and in each situation. On the basis of *the objective evidence of the films alone,* she made an estimate of fifteen behavior traits and arranged the children in rank order for each trait. After this appraisal had been recorded, she made a direct study of these same children, now 5 years old, at their homes and at the clinic. The behavior data at 5 years included an intelligence examination, performance tests, and numerous observations of the social reactions of the children to strangers, to the photographic situation, and to a tea party in which they participated. The observer made continuous stenographic notes.

After this follow-up study, the observer made a new appraisal of the original fifteen behavior traits. Care was taken to make this an independent appraisal, uninfluenced by the previous ratings which had long ago been set aside.

With these two sets of appraisals it was possible to make a comparative study of the traits of behavior individuality at 1 year and at 5 years of age. This comparison became an experiment in prediction, because we were able to ask with respect to each trait, "Is its strength in the first year of life predictive of a similar strength in the fifth year, when the five children are compared?"

The fifteen traits which were sufficiently objective to yield to clinical appraisal were as follows:

1. *Energy output* (general amount and intensity of activity).
2. *Motor demeanor* (postural bearing, general muscular control and poise, motor co-ordination, and facility of motor adjustment).
3. *Self-dependence* (general self-reliance and self-sufficiency without appeal to the assistance of others).

4. *Social responsiveness* (positive reactivity to persons and to the attitudes of adults and of other children).

5. *Family attachment* (closeness of affection; degree of identification with the family group).

6. *Communicativeness* (expressive reference to others by means of gesture and vocalization).

7. *Adaptivity* (general capacity to adjust to new situations).

8. *Exploitation of environment* (utilization and elaboration of environment and circumstances in order to gain new experience).

9. *"Humor" sense* (sensitiveness and playful reactiveness to surprise, novelty and incongruity in social situations).

10. *Emotional maladjustment* (balance and stability of emotional response in provocative situations).

11. *Emotional expressiveness* (liveliness and subtlety of expressive behavior in emotional situations).

12. *Reaction to success* (expression of satisfaction in successful endeavor).

13. *Reaction to restriction* (expressiveness of behavior in reaction to failure, discomfort, disappointment, frustration).

14. *Readiness of smiling* (facility and frequency of smiling).

15. *Readiness of crying* (promptness and facility of frowning and tears).

In spite of the fact that these categories to some extent overlap, it was found that they yielded to separate judgments based upon objective signs. Errors of judgment tended to remain uniform because they were made by a single observer. In every instance it was possible to assign with certitude the extremes of the rank order for the fifteen traits and for the group of five children. Intervening rank orders were assigned by bringing the available data into systematic comparison.

The method of cinemanalysis favored a disinterested and objective approach to the basic data. By means of a movieola and a projection desk, it was possible to subject the extensive records of infant behavior to thoroughgoing scrutiny. Significant episodes were repeatedly viewed by slowing of motion or by frame-by-frame inspection. In the field of locomotion the time values of the movements of members of the body were determined and computed for comparative purposes.

Cinemanalysis constitutes a unique method of observation, because it permits at will recurrent observation of events which in nature happen only once. The divisibility of the cinema records also permits a flexible manipulation of the data so that the recorded events can be

[129]

brought into varied forms of comparison altogether impossible in actual life.

The method of cinemanalysis therefore proved to be admirably adapted to an impersonal treatment of personality data. It should again be recalled that in the present study the cinemanalysis was made by an investigator who had had no firsthand personal contact with the children whatsoever. On the basis of detailed and critically repeated observations an array of predictions was formulated. The behavior survey at 5 years was made with sufficient thoroughness to bring any serious errors of prediction to light.

Out of the total series of 75 judgments, 48 coincided; 21 showed a displacement to the extent of one rank order; 5, a displacement of two orders; 1, a displacement of three orders. The tendency was toward underprediction. When the rank orders for each of the children are summated into grand totals, the correspondence in the net appraisal ratings at 1 year and at 5 years proves to be close: Boy D, 23, 23; Boy A, 43, 42; Girl A, 35, 45; Girl B, 53, 45; and Boy B, 71, 70.

Granting inevitable limitations in the application of the method, these results indicate a high degree of latent predictability in behavior traits manifested in the first year of life. Furthermore, the results do not suggest that fundamental individual differences increase markedly with age. The differences may become more conspicuous without undergoing a true increase.

During the treatment of the data we posed to ourselves a more difficult question, namely: *Are persisting traits of behavior individuality observable in the first sixteen weeks of life?* For three of the subjects, Boy D, Girl A, and Boy A, we had ample cinema records for testing such early predictability. When all the estimates were reviewed, it was found that the following traits were definitely noted and correctly appraised (in terms of prediction) prior to 16 weeks, in all three children: Energy output, Motor demeanor, Self-dependence, Emotional expressiveness, Readiness of smiling. For two of the children the following traits also were recognized prior to 16 weeks: Social responsiveness, Communicativeness, Adaptivity.

Every infant seems to have what may be called a motor habitude or characteristicness which expresses itself in postural demeanor and modes of movement. This characteristicness is difficult of description because it is the compound result of numerous factors, including skeletal frame, disposition of musculature, speed, synergy, smoothness and precision of action. Some of these factors yield to quantitative study.

One of the most accessible of these is laterality, and even this presented wide variation among the five individuals. By laterality we mean right or left predilection or predominance in motor adjustment. One of our infants (Girl A) showed unmistakable left-handedness as early as 28 weeks. She has remained definitely left handed for 5 years (see Chapter II). She always will be essentially left handed. Boy A showed a less marked tendency to left-handedness. Boy D has been emphatically right handed.

Foot dominance was determined by a careful study of the preferred foot used in prone progression. Boy D showed right foot dominance at 36 weeks; Boy A, left foot dominance at 40 weeks; Girl B and Boy B, left foot dominance at 48 weeks. This dominance is a well-established trait, but we do not know how late in life it persists.

In general bodily control and also in manual dexterity, the four children for whom quantitative data were secured readily fell into the following rank order: 1, Boy D; 2, Boy A; 3, Girl B; and 4, Boy B. Several hundred feet of cinema records were available for measuring the *prehension time* of these children in controlled normative situations. The interval consumed between the zero moment of reaching to the moment of grasp of the test object was computed by counting cinema frames. Each frame has a time value of .05 second. The *prehension time* (that is, the reach-grasp time) increased with the rank order as follows: Boy D (rank order one), 40 seconds; Boy A (rank order two), 47 seconds; Girl B (rank order three), 50 seconds; and Boy B (rank order four), 60 seconds.

In these time values we apparently have a rather basic trait of motor individuality, for this rank order held up with consistency when the patterns of prone progression were measured in detail. For these measurements over a thousand feet of film depicting creeping behavior were available.

Creeping speed, like prehension time, was measured by counting frames, in this instance the number of frames which recorded a forward movement of a hand or of a leg. A *creep advance* represents a single cycle of progression accomplished by a single forward placement of each of the four members. The total time required for one creep advance was determined for each of the subjects in turn. The time values ranged from .7 to 1.6 seconds for such a single creep advance. Once more the resulting rank order was identical with that just given in the preceding paragraph (see Table I).

Normally from 6 months on prone progression follows a sequence of fourteen distinguishable stages. Several of these stages were comparatively studied in our infant subjects. The simple creep advance just described represents the eleventh stage of progression and is generally characteristic of the age of 40 weeks. The *near-step advance* (stage 12, characteristic of 42 weeks) represents the next stage of progression. At this stage, the infant straightens the foot at the ankle and brings it toward a plantigrade posture without actually stepping. This new maneuver consumes additional time. The time values for this behavior pattern were determined, and again the children remained in the rank order already ascribed.

At the *one-step advance* stage (stage 13:45 weeks), the infant definitely plants the sole of his foot on the locomotion surface. This additional complication requires still more time. In this instance the time values ranged from .9 to 2.15 seconds for the four children, but again the characteristic motor rank order remained undisturbed.

Prone progression is accomplished by alternation of forward thrusts of one arm and the contralateral leg. Between these diagonal thrusts there is a palpable pause which can scarcely be observed by the naked eye, but which can be ascertained and measured by cinemanalysis. This pause diminishes in time for the three types or stages of creeping just mentioned. It however remains at any given stage highly characteristic of the individual, and accordingly the rank order for the alternation pauses remains constant for the four children.

TABLE I

Motor Traits	Boy D	Boy A	Girl B	Boy B
General control, rank order	1	2	3	4
Manual dexterity, rank order	1	2	3	4
Prehension time, rank order	1	2	3	4
Actual time	.40 sec.	.47 sec.	.50 sec.	.60 sec.
Progression:				
Creeping speed, rank order	1	2	3	4
A creep advance (Stage 11)	.70 sec.	.85 sec.	1.10 sec.	1.60 sec.
Near step advance (Stage 12)	.85 sec.	.85 sec.	1.05 sec.	2.00 sec.
One step advance (Stage 13)	.90 sec.	1.00 sec.	1.60 sec.	2.15 sec.
Alternation pause, rank order	1	2	3	4
Simple creep (Stage 11)	.65 sec.	.95 sec.	1.65 sec.	1.65 sec.
Near step (Stage 12)	.035 sec.	.04 sec.	.045 sec.	.26 sec.
One Step (Stage 13)	.05 sec.	.05 sec.	.20 sec.	.38 sec.
Age of attaining near step stage	36 wks.	40 wks.	48 wks.	48 wks.
Summated rank of ages of attaining each of 14 stages	38	43	70	78
Laterality				
Age of foot dominance	36 wks.	40 wks.	48 wks.	48 wks.
Dominant foot	Right	Left	Left	Left
Dominant hand ..	Right++	L-R (28 wks.)	Right	Right

Another individual difference asserted itself with respect to the age at which the various stages of prone locomotion were attained. For example, the ages when the near-step stage was attained were as follows: Boy D, 36 weeks; Boy A, 40 weeks; Girl B, 48 weeks; Boy B, 48 weeks.

When the nascent ages for the entire sequence of fourteen stages in the ontogenesis of progression are expressed in terms of summated rank for each of the four children we get a significant series of values: Boy D, 38; Boy A, 43; Girl B, 70; Boy B, 78. Again the rank order remains true to the characteristic order established by the measurement of specific motor traits.

The accompanying table summarizes these measurements based upon frame by frame cinemanalysis.

In general the most accurate predictions were made for Boy D and for Boy B. These two boys presented contrastive behavior traits, which we may now summarize, if the reader will kindly understand that we do not suggest that one set of traits is necessarily superior to the other set. Each boy, like each of us, is in his psychological make-up a mixture of assets and some liabilities.

As early as the ages of 8 and 12 weeks the highly dynamic personality of Boy D made a strong impression even when observed only through the medium of the cinema. After a full year of recorded behavior had been subjected to such inspection the following adjectives were used to characterize his individuality: quick, active, happy, friendly, well adjusted, vigorous, forceful, alert, inquisitive. Although he was definitely extrovertive he showed at the early age of 24 weeks a surprising discriminativeness in reading the facial expressions of his mother. By the age of 28 weeks he had developed a moderate temper technique for influencing domestic situations which did not altogether please him. He was able to shift quickly in his emotional response from smiling to crying and from crying to smiling to achieve a desired end. At the age of 5 years, likewise, his emotional reactions are labile and versatile. He is facile in changing his emotional responses. He is highly perceptive of emotional expressions in others and, correspondingly, highly adaptive in social situations. With this emotional alertness he shows a relatively vigorous detachment from his mother as well as affection for her. He is not given to persisting moods. We do not get the impression that his emotional characteristics have been primarily determined by his life experiences. The underlying nature of his "emotivity" at 12 weeks, at 52 weeks, and at 260 weeks seems rather constant. With altered outward configurations a certain characteristicness in emotional reactions is quite likely to persist into his later life.

Boy B presents a different constellation of characteristics. Although by no means emotionally shallow, he is by comparison less vivid, less expressive, more self-contained than Boy D. He is a sturdy, deliberate, moderately sociable, friendly child whose characteristics were evident at 1 year as well as at 5 years.

Boy B still shows motor ineptnesses and inhibitions comparable to those which he displayed in infancy. Boy D, on the other hand, has given consistent evidence of superior motor co-ordination from an early age in postural control, locomotion and manual dexterity. At 20 weeks he manipulated a string of wooden beads with precocious discriminativeness; at 44, he actuated a hinged rattle with a clever screwdriver movement of the wrists; at 1 year he pulled out an electric plug in an adaptive manner. At 2 years he repeatedly inserted and reinserted electric plugs, adjusted bridge lamps, latched and unlatched doors, and operated an egg beater. The drive and deftness of his ceaseless manipulation strongly suggest in this instance mechanical insight and aptitude.

We have devoted a paragraph to motor traits because they best lend themselves to objective statement. If other traits of individuality become equally amenable to measurement and appraisal, applied psychology will be increasingly concerned with the detection of individual differences in the first year of life. With the aid of the cinema our exploratory study has demonstrated a significant degree of internal consistency in the behavior features of the same children at 1 and at 5 years of age. This consistency seems to rest upon biological characteristicness; a characteristicness which as yet can not be quantitatively formulated in a satisfactory manner but which is incontrovertible.

Our findings must not be overgeneralized, but they strongly indicate that certain fundamental traits of individuality, whatever their origin, exist early, persist late, and assert themselves under varying environmental conditions. This does not mean that physical and cultural environments have no influence upon a growing organism. It is suggested, however, that this influence may be properly envisaged as operating upon and subject to basic constitutional characters. The extrinsic environment impresses circumstantial and topical configurations, but a certain *naturel* is given, and it is for this reason that we discover such early evidences of individuality in the human infant.

Since we must tread warily in this field of discourse, we shall conclude with a vague but pregnant passage from Shakespeare:

A man may prophesy with a near aim of the chance of things, as yet not come to life, which in their seeds and weak beginnings lie intreasured. Such things become the hatch and brood of time.

CHAPTER XIII

Genius, Giftedness, and Growth*

The topic originally suggested for this paper by the program committee was the vast and protean subject of "Genius." I attempted to contract the theme by limiting it to the more manageable dimensions of the subtitle, "Creative Behavior in Child and Adult"! But I find this only adds to our difficulties, because on close examination it appears that every normal infant is by nature a creative artist of sorts. Indeed the poet Schiller long ago observed that if we all lived up to the promise of our infancies we should all be geniuses. So, where does genius begin, and where does it end? Why do the Wordsworthian prison shades close in?

When asked to give the very shortest definition of life, Claude Bernard, the great physiologist, answered, "Life is creation." We may think of creative behavior as the highest manifestation of life—a manifestation mediated by the nervous system. At a sheer biochemical level there is some creation, even in respiration, for respiration is a process of synthesis and transformation. Plants as well as animals respire. A genius accomplishes his syntheses and tranformations at a cultural level. He brings into being original forms of behavior of unique value to the society into which he is born. His contribution is more socialized than mere respiration. It demands a nervous system of high order, with distinctive urges capable of bursting the confines of custom.

* Lectures to the Laity, New York Academy of Medicine, New York, February 1942.

The mystically inclined would interpret the works of genius as the result of occult forces which operate upon man's subconscious, which take hold of him thaumaturgically, and possess him with daemonic energy. The very word genius sometimes means a tutelary god, a spirit or a demon. But this romantic concept is too dualistic, too animistic for our purposes. It is too supernatural. Our task is to make the operations of creative behavior, including genius, more understandable, by interpreting them in the light of universal natural processes.

We shall therefore use the child as a touchstone, to define and to illustrate those functions of the nervous system which bear the hallmark of genius.

THE INFANT AS CREATOR

To take the whole subject somewhat out of the mists I shall presently call to our aid photographic illustrations and diagrams. Remembering that the infant is a novice devoid of all mundane experience, you may well be amazed at his resourcefulness, his "extraordinary capacity for original activity, invention and discovery," which, by the way, is the dictionary definition of genius itself!

Is the infant indeed a genius? Or is he not the extremest polar opposite of a genius, if by genius, we mean a creator who makes a concrete, distinctive contribution to culture? For the human infant is a pathetically helpless parasite upon culture, an arrant novice. And yet he is also a brilliant innovator. Here is a paradox, which may amuse, but need not confuse.

A baby is not only a specific embodiment of a future adult; he is a generic embodiment of the venerable past of the human race. He represents a vast cloud of ancestral witnesses compacted into a single individuality. He is inheritor of the ages. His nervous system is the carrier of an immense series of evolutionary adaptations, by means of which the race consolidated its most essential achievements. These achievements are now the common property of mankind; but *once they were creations*. The evolution of the human species has been a creative process on a cosmic scale. The human infant as the current

[138]

custodian of that process revives in telescoped compression its immemorial creativity. Once more in little theater he renders a fluent
series of dramatic sketches of his phyletic biography. He does, *de novo,*
what the race has already done. He acts like a creator because he is
basically a re-creator of what happened long ago, once upon a time.
He is an innovator because he is a rehearser. Thereby hangs the
novice-genius paradox. Infancy is both conclusion and preface.

Setting all paradox aside let us examine the architecture of the
nervous system of this infant, and the resultant patterns of behavior.
For the nervous system is the architectonic instrument which brings
into being all forms of behavior from mediocre to transcendent.
(Chapter II.)

Fetal nervous system.   In Fig. 1 you have a photographic rendering
of a 5-month-old fetus, and a diagrammatic hint of the twelve billions
of protoplasmic cells and the unimaginable myriad of fibers and fibrils
which constitute the nervous system—three vast networks of receptor,
effector, and intermediary neurones combined into one integral and
integrating fabric. It is this fabric which preserves the unity of the
organism and embodies the psychological individuality of fetus, infant,
child, and adult. (Interestingly enough by the fetal age of 5 months
the future adult has already acquired his full and final quota of
neurones.)

Now the most significant feature of this intricate network of nerve
fibers and filaments is its enormous capacity for growth. The growth
is a process of organization, whereby the neurones come into functional
relationship evidenced in patterns of behavior. The fetus purses its
lips, the neonate makes throaty sounds, the infant vocalizes words, the
child speaks sentences. The race acquired articulate speech by similar
gradations. Whether the sentences of the adult prove to have any of the
essence of genius will depend in some unknown way upon the quality
and the maturity of the mediating neurones, all of which are subject
to a physiology of development. The whole problem of genius and
creative behavior is one of relativity. It is always concerned with
gradations of growth.

In our investigations at Yale we have charted the early growth of behavior patterns by recording the progressive reactions of the infant to various test objects. Significant patterns were elicited at lunar-month intervals by a wooden, one-inch cube, painted red after the tradition of the nursery.

The progression in these patterns illustrates the nature of all mental growth:

Age 4 weeks. Reflex in clasp (tactile cue).
Age 12 weeks. Ocular fixation (visual cue).
Age 24 weeks. Prehension on sight (eye-hand co-ordination).
Age 40 weeks. Poking palpation (specialization of index).
Age 52 weeks. Digital grasp and release (thumb opposition).

These are lawful progressions, necessary sequences of maturation determined in the egg. They are creative events in the same sense as embryogenesis *is genesis.* They are the natural prerequisites for creative exploitations at higher levels of maturity.

The geometry of growth.   Now for a closer look at the configurations of cube behavior. In Fig. 2 you see them in outline, for the first 5 years of life. Note how the infant invades and conquers the sectors of space, the vertical (V), the horizontal (H) and the oblique (O). These are ontogenetic sequences, inflected but not engendered by environment: "Nature geometrizeth," said Plato. You see how with gradual creativeness, nature combines the horizontal (H) and vertical components (V) of the movement repertoire, to bring about new combinations, and even new syntheses. She originates out of her geometry the oblique dimension, and is not the oblique a synthetic deflection of H and V, which produces neither H nor V, but can be rationalized by the equation $\frac{1}{2}H + \frac{1}{2}V = O = Oblique!$

At any rate this block-building sequence is offered as a paradigm, which represents the *modus operandi* of the more recondite and inaccessible processes of creative behavior.

Age	Action and Structure	Directional Component
12 wks.	Fixates, 1 block	H+V (ocular)
20 wks.	Corrals, 1 block	H (manual)
28 wks.	Bangs, 1 block	V (exploitation)
40 wks.	Matches, 2 blocks	H (combining)
1 year	Superimposes, 1 block	$V+\frac{1}{2}V$ (incipient alignment)
18 mos.	Tower, 3 blocks	V (alignment)
2 years	Wall, 3 blocks	H (alignment)
3 years	Bridge, 3 blocks	V+V+H (construction)
4 years	Gate, 3 or 5 blocks	$V+V+(\frac{1}{2}V+\frac{1}{2}H)=V+V+$Oblique
5 years	Staircase, 6 blocks	H+H+H+V+V+H

The ontogenesis of block building. Fig. 2 affords a panoramic view of ten levels of exploitive behavior, with the one-inch cube as stimulus and foil. For the infant these seriated block structures and exploitations are so many creative acts, the ontogenetic products of a growing nervous system. They are not derived from culture. Only to a small degree are they fashioned by imitation, because the child cannot even imitate successfully until he has acquired through maturation the requisite neuromotor equipment. (This, by the way, is one reason most of us are unable to imitate a genius.) For the race these seriated advances were also in the nature of creative achievements. They portray in outline the slow growth and limitations of primitive intelligence. These "simple" conquests of geometry were inevitable, indispensable, basic, in the evolution of the race. They reappear as developmental stages in the individual. Even Leonardo da Vinci, master artist and engineer, had to traverse them.

The great Leonardo, however, was more than an ordinary representative of his species, and in his preschool childhood he must have given promise of his later distinction. It would be most interesting to have his performance on our normative developmental schedules. When he was 4 years old, what manner of man did he draw? Was it a primitive, potatolike oval with two appendages, characteristic of an ordinary child of 4? Probably not.

Precocious drawing talent. Fig. 3 pictures the artistic productions of a gifted girl at 3 years, 5 months; 3 years, 6 months; and 3 years, 7 months. Her superiority is evident. The first drawing, at 3 years, 5 months, already surpasses the drawings of an average 5-year-old child. And note how swiftly her talent grows from one month to another. This was prophetic talent. It was also reminiscent in the sense that she was born of artistic ancestors.

At the age of 15 years she drew an ironic fashion figure with delicate modernistic strokes, showing a predilection for the same slender elongated composition which was characteristic of her preschool years —an interesting example of indigenous individuality of style. Artistic ability tends to manifest itself early. As an adolescent this girl showed it in three directions: music, sensitive diction, and drawing. We shall not call her a genius; but her superiority over mediocrity suggests the very qualities which, sufficiently enhanced, constitute genius.

The Incomplete Man Test. Such differences in the gradient of creativity show themselves very transparently in certain tests of the adaptive behavior at preschool ages, such as the Incomplete Man Test. We present an outline drawing of this partial man and simply say to the child, "You finish him." Each child responds in terms of his maturity, capacity, and individuality. Figure 6 illustrates the paucity and obtuseness of a subnormal response, a crude filling in and a doubtful second leg.

The responses of average and superior children are also pictured at 2½, 3, 4, and 5 years of age. Acceleration is again evident in the superiors. But still more significant is their greater range of elaboration. The average 3-year-old supplies an accessory scribble; it is a vague, generalized addition, grossly placed. It is responsive, it is intelligent, but it is meager.

Compare the imagery and the executions of the superior 3-year-old who with discriminating placement supplies missing leg, shoes, arm, hands, eyes, and umbilicus; but still is not satisfied. Her assimilative mind moves toward further completion so she projects her anatomically completed man against a Christmas tree, not forgetting the trunk of the tree. But even this is not enough, so in the corner goes a doorknob, with a keyhole. For her all these components somehow hang together or even synthesize. She is engaged in productive integrative thinking; her emotional reactions, moreover, are much richer than those of her "average" compeer. Running comments, soliloquy, and conversation, also, are much more abundant in the gifted children. These differences are both quantitative and qualitative; for the superior child is more originative. He thinks, articulates, and contrives completions, which never occur to the more modestly endowed child even at a more advanced age.

It is well to point out here that creative behavior is not synonymous with *Quiz Kids* or even with *Information Please*. Indeed the present vogue of memory feats has somewhat obscured the significance of intelligence. Creative behavior is not identical with a high I.Q. Coleridge, to be sure, has been archaeologically credited with an I.Q. of 164; but on the same scale Darwin rated 125; Copernicus, 130; and poor Sir Francis Drake only 110. Evidently there is no direct, invariable correlation between I.Q. and eminence. And it is sadly true that a high I.Q. is often associated with meager creativity.

When, however, acceleration of development is accompanied by an intensified, well-integrated behavior organization, it is a normal symptom of giftedness. We know of a well-constituted, active boy (real but anonymous), who has displayed this happy combination of traits since infancy. He is 16 years old, but had attained an adult level of psychometric intelligence at the age of 8 years, when he earned an intelligence quotient of approximately 200.

The subjoined table tells the story of acceleration:

Accelerated		Usual
Clearly articulates many words	1 yr.	2 yrs.
Alphabet (150 words)	1½ yrs.	4 yrs.
Read stories	3 yrs.	7 yrs.
Tales from Shakespeare	4 yrs.	11 yrs.
Entered Junior High School	7 yrs.	12 yrs.
Completed plane geometry	8 yrs.	15 yrs.
Four-year college chemistry course	9 yrs.	18–22 yrs.
Passes college entrance exams	10 yrs.	18 yrs.
Entered college	13 yrs.	18 yrs.
Phi Beta Kappa	16 yrs.	22 yrs.
Advanced postgraduate work	16 yrs.	25 yrs.

Exploitation and experimentation. To demonstrate the dynamic quality of creative behavior we must resort to the cinema.[1] Behavior patterns are living forms which take visible shape upon the silver screen, just as they take concealed shape in the electronic recesses of the nervous system. By coincident projection it is possible to gain a simultaneous view of the cube behavior of the selfsame infant at 24 weeks and at 28 weeks. At 24 weeks he gives exclusive banging and mouthing attention to one cube; at 28 weeks he grasps two cubes, one in either hand, attends to each and even sketchily combines them. The difference between these two behavior pictures·represents an increment of growth. The 40-week-old infant shows a striking advance in his "creative" manipulation of three cubes.

At 48 weeks he shows well-defined exploration and experimentation with a small hand bell—seizes it by the handle, waves it, transfers it from hand to hand, rotates it, inspects, listens; pokes his index pryingly into the bowl. Such versatile variations of self-induced exploitation remind us of Schiller's aphorism, that we should indeed be geniuses if we lived up to these infant tokens of initiative and originality.

These tokens are characteristic of normal infancy. Contrast them with the impoverished behavior of a subnormal child, or of one who has been thwarted by excessive institutional life or perhaps by a cerebral injury. The defective child often displays extremely stereotyped behavior, constricted to a narrow repetitious pattern. His "exploitations" completely lack originality. They are not exploitations at all; they are stereotypes. In idiocy these stereotypes become permanent automatisms. The stereotypy of idiocy is the very antithesis of creativeness.

Contrast them in turn with the drawings of the highly endowed girl of kindergarten age whose drawing of a man concludes our film. She cannot restrain her elaborations when the artist's mood is upon her. She cannot stay within stereotyped nor conventional bounds. She has

[1] A film was shown to illustrate certain clinical and developmental aspects of creative behavior. The film was based on cinema records of the Photographic Research Library of the Yale Clinic of Child Development.

too many images and details to express: fingers, teeth, eyebrows, duck, multiple ducklings, and an earthworm for them to eat. She is not only growing; she is burgeoning. She is displaying precociously that quality of imaginativeness which so often foretells creative ability in the adult.

THE CREATIVE IMAGINATION IN POETRY

It is time now to consider the adult, and those forms of creative behavior which the world acknowledges and treasures as genius. How can we make the transition to such exalted levels? And shall we need new concepts to explain the psychology of full-blown genius? We may well turn to poetry for light on these questions. Words are authentic clues to the thought processes of genius. Modes of language are "the working modes of the mind." They are patterns of behavior. And poetry is the supreme use of language. It has been called man's chief co-ordinating instrument in the service of the most integral purposes of life.

We turn, therefore, to Samuel Taylor Coleridge, a unique poetic genius. He wrote two of the most beautiful poems in the English language: "The Rime of the Ancient Mariner" and "Kubla Khan."

Intrigued by their power and perfection, the late John L. Lowes, Professor of English, Harvard University, undertook to chart the genesis of these unparalleled poems, in a sizable tome of 22 chapters and 1,104 footnotes, entitled *The Road to Xanadu*.[2] His volume is a superb piece of detective work, detailed, meticulous, scholarly, almost clinical. He ransacked hundreds of books, tracts, letters, and journals, seeking clues to Coleridge's creative condensations, "to discover how, in two great poems, out of chaos the imagination frames a thing of beauty."

The Road to Xanadu leads back to Coleridge's childhood. He read chapters from the Bible at 3. The very sight of the book cover of *Arabian Nights Entertainments* filled him, he says with "a strange mixture of obscure dread and intense desire. . . . My whole being

[2] *The Road to Xanadu; a Study in the Ways of the Imagination* (Boston, 1927).

was with eyes closed to every object of present sense, to crumple myself up in a sunny corner, and read, read, read."

He read with the same passionate intensity as an adult, his mind luminous with visual imagery, and coruscating associations. When his imagination worked at high tension during metrical composition, he seemed to be capable of eidetic imagery—distinct, luminous, quasi-perceptual revivals of previous experience. "Vivid spectra," he called them.

Great poetry is superlative condensation. If we knew how Coleridge managed to condense and select from the wealth of imagery which weltered as in a "deep well," we should know more of the mechanism of creation. He was dependent upon omnivorous reading and a photographic memory. He read, for example, Captain Cook's *Voyage,* Priestley's *Opticks,* and a volume of *Philosophical Transactions,* with their scattered references to colored animalculae, phosphorescence from putrescence, and the shining wake of ships. Long afterward these multifarious impressions, slumbering in the deep well came to con-centrated confluence in forty-six words, forty of which are mono-syllables.

> The very deep did rot: O Christ!
> That ever this should be!
> Yea, slimy things did crawl with legs
> Upon the slimy sea.
>
> About, about, in reel and rout
> The death-fires danced at night;
> The water, like witch's oils.
> Burnt green, and blue and white.

How utterly these eight lines are removed from prolixity! Prolixity merely rehearses. Creative genius selects, distills, eliminates. Coleridge, as James Russell Lowell remarked, gives us "the very quintessence of perception, the clearly crystallized precipitation of all that is most precious in the ferment of impression after the impertinent and obtrusive particulars have evaporated from the memory. It is the pure visual ecstasy disengaged from the confused and confusing material that gave it birth."

This disengagement is essentially a developmental process. It is a differentiation of structure leading to specific ends. It is not unlike the disengagement which takes place in the limb bud of a growing embryo when five fingers emerge out of a rudimentary stump.

"The Ancient Mariner" was a growth phenomenon in more senses than one. It did not spring Minerva-like from the poet's brow. Wordsworth who had a hand in the original planning of the poem, said that it "grew and grew." It grew from half-past four in the afternoon of November 13, 1797, to March 23, 1798, when Coleridge went to drive with Wordsworth and brought him the finished ballad. But the growth started long before that, when a little boy of kindergarten age crumpled himself up in a sunny corner to read, and read, and read.

One critic, John Mackinnon Robertson, suggests that Coleridge's "Mariner" was one of the chance blooms of a season of physiological ecstasy, the ecstasy being induced by the use of opium. The explanation is too simple and does not take account of the laborious and deliberate craftsmanship which went into the final design of the poem. Nor can opium account for the multifarious imagery and the myriad of words and contexts which grew as though in a cultivated garden during the years before the anodyne. Even chance "blooms" must come from seeds.

There is no doubt that "Kubla Khan" was composed under the influence of opium. The poet fell asleep in his chair at the moment that he was reading, in *Purchas his Pilgrimage,* a sentence about Khan Kubla commanding a palace to be built. During sleep he apparently composed some two hundred lines of poetry without any consciousness of effort. On waking he eagerly wrote down the famous lines (which were never completed because of the interruption of a visitor on business).

[147]

In Xanadu did Kubla Khan
A stately pleasure-dome decree:
Where Alph, the sacred river, ran
Through caverns measureless to man
Down to a sunless sea.

There is an almost uncanny quality of somnambulism about this poem. The imagery has the "streaming randomness" of a dream, but it is couched in musical rhythms. Opium might release the images and the melody but it could scarcely create them. The sure flights of the rhythms, as Lowes suggests, "sprang from a control achieved through the assiduous elaboration, in 'The Ancient Mariner' and 'Christabel,' of a metrical technique." Coleridge worked before he slept.

Genius may have effortless moments which suggest inspiration, but these moments are usually preceded by prolonged periods of preparation. So-called unconscious cerebration can take place only as a result of purposeful endeavor. Goethe who is sometimes regarded as an inspired writer acknowledged that "men of greatest genius and talent are ever and ceaselessly demanding of themselves diligent application which is needful in their development."

The creative imagination is not a faculty nor an indwelling spirit which at moments of divine afflatus emerges from the recesses to grapple with raw materials. It is rather an acquired personal possession, structured out of experiences and strivings, a living system which has undergone a developmental organization and is still actively growing.

The Creative Imagination in Science

This is as true of the scientific as of the artistic imagination. The scientific genius is a prodigious worker, endowed with persevering patience. Through zeal, curiosity, and sheer labor he amasses within himself an immense complex of observations and concepts. This complex becomes so engrossing that it almost possesses him. But he really possesses it and projects it toward advancing purposes. It is a dynamic system which grows with what it feeds on, sets up new tensions leading to new patterns. Some of the patterns may have an element of surprise and of dramatic discovery, but the basic gains are increments of gradual growth.

So it was with Charles Darwin, who declared "It's dogged as does it." (Perhaps he was thinking of the dog who went to Dover leg over leg.) He was self-taught and he held with Galton that mental qualities are largely innate. The systematic self-teaching began with the voyage of the *Beagle*. Darwin collected facts on a wholesale scale, opening his first notebook in 1837. He started observations on the earthworm a year or two later. Just before his death, he published the volume which bore the title, *Formation of Vegetable Mould through the Action of Worms* (1881). He worked on the volume forty-two years. The earthworms by constantly raising earth from below the surface brought up a layer 9 inches deep in the same length of time.

Darwin had an overpowering tendency to generalize and to theorize, a passion for ideological order. It was part of his genius that he had no pride of opinion. He was especially keen to notice exceptions and small variations which easily escape attention. He strove for a concept which would fit all the facts. Hence the boldness and sweep of his theory of evolution. Paradoxically, yet prophetically, he was no stickler for "facts" when he was an 8-year-old boy. At that age he was given to inventing deliberate falsehoods and was able to fabricate monstrous fables. Was this, perhaps, a preliminary symptom of his adult creative hypotheses?

Josiah Willard Gibbs (1839-1903) was a transcendent genius. He had, it is now belatedly acknowledged, the most creative scientific mind that America has produced. In many of his moral and intellectual characteristics he resembled Darwin; but unlike him he deployed his powers almost entirely in the abstract realms of mathematical symbols, statistics, and geometric diagrams of laws and physical forces (Darwin was almost devoid of mathematical ability).

Gibbs was a mathematical physicist and chemist combined, "the greatest synthetic philosopher since Newton," the founder of physical chemistry and the science of chemical energetics, on which American industry so largely rests. "Just as Newton first conclusively showed that this is a world of masses, so Willard Gibbs first revealed it as a world of systems."

So profound and fertile was his creative thinking with respect to the equilibrium of heterogeneous substances, their thermodynamic properties and statistical mechanics, that his principles have application to living as well as nonliving systems. So profound were his ideas that it took another genius, a Scotch one, James C. Maxwell, to recognize them early.

Gibbs himself was serenely unconscious of his intellectual profundity. To an intimate friend, he said, with delightfully simple candor, "If I have had any success in mathematical physics, it is, I think because I have been able to dodge mathematical difficulties!"

His mind moved with uncanny, masterful precision, after periods of concentrated reflection. He wrote with extraordinary succinctness, invariable accuracy, and rigorous elegance. His papers, Hastings remarks, imply vast and systematic industry. His contributions did not depend upon experiments, nor upon special hypotheses as to the constitution of matter, but on experimental laws. "To have obtained the results . . . in any manner would have been a great achievement; that they were reached by a method of such logical austerity is a still greater cause for wonder and admiration."

The logical austerity of this great thinker continued to his end. He kept growing. His last work, regarded by some as his greatest, was published shortly before his death in his sixty-fourth year. In this work he returned to the theme of Statistical Mechanics which had interested him in his thirties or even earlier. Which recalls a definition to the effect that "Genius is an idea of youth developed in maturity." The book was written after long years of sheer meditation. It was composed almost without notes and completed in less than a year. L. J. Henderson calls it "perhaps the greatest example of sustained thought in the history of America."

For over thirty years he served as Professor of Mathematical Physics at Yale College, from where he had graduated in 1858. It is comforting to add that the greatest American genius (and a professor besides) was neither absent-minded nor eccentric. He did not work by inspiration; he could stop his thinking any time to speak with a student; he was friendly, approachable, had a ready smile, a lively sense of humor, was fond of children. He was inherently modest, of gentle, judicial temperament. And yet a practical man of affairs. He was so well balanced that there is scarcely an anecdote ascribed to him.

Gibbs does not support the notion that genius is to madness close allied. He fails to fit into Alexis Carrel's characterization of men of genius; "ill-balanced, unhappy beings, with tumorous overgrowth, as disharmonious as the criminal and the insane." In personality Gibbs had no evident peculiarities; although it is true he never married. From the age of 30 to his death at 64, he lived with an elder, married sister in a house built by his father. Such a circumstance tells us little about the origins of genius; nor does it account for comparable bachelors who did not become geniuses. Darwin, by contrast, was the father of ten children. Darwin's genius is interpreted (by Kempf) in terms of a chronic anxiety neurosis induced by his relations with his father, the recurrent gastric attacks being in the nature of "unconscious delaying mechanisms."

Similarly, creativeness in poetry and the plastic arts has been ascribed to varied psychoanalytic mechanisms: a) transformed sexual energy; b) unconscious restoration of persons destroyed in phantasy; c) confessions of guilt over unconscious incestuous phantasies; d) synergistic and serial unconscious mental processes through which the artist transcends the miseries of recurrent mobile depressions. The artist heals with "the balm of creating beauty as an esthetic salvation, that excess guilt, dread of the loss of love, and anxiety over generative integrity which resulted from his latest explosion" (H. B. Levey).

These interpretations I mention for the record, without any attempt to appraise them. They represent a dualistic approach to the problem of creative behavior and emphasize the concept of psychogenetic conflict where I would first of all utilize the monistic, biological concept of growth. Whatever the fate of these speculations they must finally take account of those determinants of creative behavior which are so deep-seated that they express themselves long before adult conflicts come to definition. The primary determiners of genius undoubtedly reside in genetic constitution, and we shall never arrive at the inner nature of genous until we know more about the nature of growth.

Genius and Growth

Genius is a growth phenomenon. The psychobiography of genius is full of embryological and horticultural terms, references to its brooding qualities, to germination, incubation, efflorescence. The very word genial means conducive to growth; and in an old sense a genius chamber was a bridal chamber. Shakespeare has imagination body forth the forms of things unknown, and makes Time a nurse, a breeder, a begetter, which molds

> . . . the chance of things
> As yet not come to life, which in their seeds
> And weak beginnings lie intreasured.
> Such things become the hatch and brood of Time.

Genius implies gestation, whether we think of specific arts of creation or the longer reaches of the life cycle. In some persons it is the total life career rather more than individual accomplishments which denotes their genius. Such a person was Abraham Lincoln. His career is a striking example of the configuring forces of a slow and steady growth. He was slow minded, retarded in repartee, not distinguished for inspired feats of brilliance. As a tall, blue-shinned youth he was an irresistibly funny talker. In his early maturity his poetry was doggerel, his lectures ornate, his speeches somewhat bombastic. Not until he was in his forty-sixth year did his public utterance rise to the dignity, breadth, and sympathy which came to characterize his diction. His Springfield speech of 1854 was the prelude to the Gettysburg Address, the Bixby letter, and the exalted cadences of the Second Inaugural. The evolution of his literary style reflects the development of his genius. He was slowly seasoned by the times which he himself did so much to create. In perspective, his life career takes on the dimensions and the design of a myth, because there was a profound correspondence between his peculiar genius and the culture in which he grew.

Cultures like individuals seem to obey laws of growth and to have their periods of bloom, of birth and rebirth. Lincoln's great Springfield speech belonged to that golden half-decade between 1850 and 1855 which marked the American Renaissance and saw the appearance in succession of Emerson's essay, *Representative Men,* Hawthorne's *Scarlet Letter,* Melville's *Moby Dick,* Thoreau's *Walden,* and Whitman's *Leaves of Grass.* F. O. Matthiessen[3] has just written a sympathetic critique of this era of imaginative vitality.

Melville's masterpiece is especially pertinent for us, because it vividly reflects the interaction between a genius and the matrix of the age into which he was born. That interaction is embodied in one of the most original characters in all fiction, Ahab, the fanatic Quaker huntsman of the White Whale. That character was created in the heat of imagination, but he was also inherent in the constitution of contemporary society. He was not a figment of fancy, but a profound derivation drawn from realities. Melville himself noted that a genuine original had to have such an origin, "it being as true in literature as in Zoology, that all life is from the egg."

Moby Dick is at once "the finest piece of dramatic writing in American literature," "the best tragic epic of modern times," and "one of the supreme poetic monuments of the English language." In this volume, "Melville achieved the deep integrity of that double vision which sees with both eyes—the scientific eye of actuality, and the illumined eye of imagination and dream."

[3] *American Renaissance: Art and Expression in the Age of Emerson and Whitman* (London, 1941).

Meditation and water are wedded forever, said Melville. Listen to the "incantatory rhythms" of two memorable sentences in which he expresses the solemn symbolism of the Pacific Ocean. The sentences have a new poignancy since the infamous seventh of December, 1941.

The Pacific

There is, one knows not what sweet mystery about this sea, whose gentle awful stirrings seem to speak of some hidden soul beneath; like those fabled undulations of the Ephesian sod over the buried evangelist St. John. And meet it is, that over these sea-pastures, wide-rolling watery prairies and Potter's Fields of all four continents, the waves should rise and fall, and ebb and flow unceasingly; for here, millions of mixed shades and shadows, drowned dreams, somnambulisms, reveries; all that we call lives and souls, lie dreaming, dreaming, still; tossing like slumberers in their beds; the everrolling waves but made so by their restlessness.

In *Moby Dick*, Melville reached the peak of his creative powers. He was only 32 years old. Although chronologically in his prime, with forty more years to live, he never recaptured the imaginative energy which produced his masterpiece. This fact brings into sharp relief the dependence of creative vitality upon the equilibrium of the underlying factors of growth. In the complex epic of the White Whale these factors converged into a dynamic focus. All that went before was by way of developmental preparation.

Some of these developmental determinants can now be identified. Even as a child, Herman Melville showed reflectiveness and independence of mind. At the age of 6 he was described as "both solid and profound." His adolescence was full of conflicts and uncertainties, aggravated by the death of an oversainted father. At 17 he went to sea, to cut loose from his mother and sympathizing kin. In more than one sense he learned the ropes. He girdled the globe, sailing in a trader, a man-o'-war, and a whaler. He met with all kinds and conditions of men. He saw the dives of Liverpool and the more Edenic islands of Polynesia. He talked with man-eating epicures, mutineers, and missionaries. He passed long night watches under tropical stars, pondering both stars and men, "serenely concocting information into wisdom."

A tossing crow's-nest preceded the desk from which he wrote, ". . . if, at my death, my executors or more properly my creditors find any precious manuscript in my desk, then here I prospectively ascribe all the honor and the glory to whaling; for a whale ship was my Yale College and my Harvard."

And to top off this marvelous curriculum of intense living, what did Melville do? He read the entire works of Shakespeare, read them, fortunately, as a mature man, when he could meditate upon their meaning creatively. "Dolt and ass that I am," he then exclaimed, "I have lived more than twenty-nine years and until a few days ago, never made close acquaintance with the divine William. Ah, he's full of sermons-on-the-mount, and gentle, ay, almost as Jesus."

Melville dated his creative life from his twenty-fifth year, the year when he returned from the sea. In the next seven years he wrote seven books, *Moby Dick* being the sixth. It was a burgeoning period. He was intensely, almost joyously conscious of the plenitude of his powers. He felt that to create a mighty book you must choose a mighty theme. He chose Leviathan. "Give me," he exclaimed, "a condor's quill! Give me Vesuvius' crater for an inkstand! Friends, Hold my arms!"

In the throes of composition he felt the moods of King Lear, and the stimulus of Shakespeare, "the most abundant imagination in history." His styles of utterance were profoundly transformed. Geniuses fructify each other. This was a true morphogenesis—a developmental phenomenon on a grand scale, in which great patterns *by induction* engendered great patterns. To behold the configuration of the resultant patterns, you must read *Moby Dick*, which is literally a pageant of unparalleled patterns, still radiant with the warmth of their creation.

Strangely enough, Melville saw that this was the culmination of his powers, for in a letter to Hawthorne he wrote, "I feel that I am now come to the inmost bulb, and that shortly the flower must fall to the mould." And it was true. Note how in his very metaphors, Melville supports our thesis, that there is something vegetative and morphogenetic about creative behavior. Genius is a way of growth.

[155]

Being a way of growth, its full manifestation in a poorly integrated artist is dependent upon a very happy convergence of conditions, both internal and external. That convergence in Melville and also in Coleridge was tragically brief. Only for one short period did Coleridge launch himself upon "a magnificent voyage into the unreal and make it real. It was his one hour of pure creative satisfaction, but it was a miracle that hung upon the hazard of circumstance and which circumstance did not allow him to repeat." The flower fell.

The Developmental Physiology of Genius

For these reasons we may look into the physiology of development for clues as to the nature of genius. Our task is not the impossible one of explaining the mystery of creative behavior; we shall be content to suggest its conditions in terms of mechanisms about which something is known. We turn, therefore, to the science of experimental embryology; for our problem in some manner has to do with embryogenesis, the origins of living form. Melville himself you recall, profoundly hinted that in creative literature as in zoology all life is from the egg. Let us, accordingly, examine the egg.

To simplify our thinking we shall represent egg, embryo, and organism alike by a diagrammatic oval in Fig. 7. The experimental embryologist, for convenience, works largely with newts, salamanders, frogs, and chicks; but for our own convenience we shall let the same diagram serve for all orders of life, including *homo sapiens*, even at the genius level, because we wish to inquire whether there are some common factors, which may help to define the nature of creative behavior.

Egg: genes, arranged warp-woof-wise in chromosomes. The egg is packed with enzymatic particles, giant molecules, perhaps, called genes. It is not a pun to say that these genes carry the primary determiners of genius itself. They have a capacity to propagate and to reorganize surrounding molecules.

[156]

Embryo: an electrodynamic pattern. With fertilization the egg becomes a living system. An electrodynamic field emerges. This field extends beyond the physical periphery of the organism. It is determined by the cellular components, and also determines them. It maintains a wholeness of pattern from the very beginning. The embryo is perfectly integrated even before it has a nervous system.

Chimerical embryo: host and implant. This fantastic creature is a product of experimental embryology. The experimenter has surgically grafted into a living embryo, at varying times, three small bits of tissue from another embryo, thereby evoking structures A, B, and C. The experiment demonstrates the profundity and inveterateness of the creative essence of growth. (This is the essence which genius recaptures.) The morphological fate of the implants is determined 1) by the genes; 2) by their space-location in the topography of the protoplasm; 3) by their time-location in the growth cycle. In normal development these factors interact harmoniously within and through the electrodynamic field. In the experimental deviation of development the form of each structure depends upon space-time factors. A becomes a secondary cephalic head, B a caudad head, C a supernumerary caudad tail! In a growing system the components are in a state of labile equilibrium. One component has the capacity to *induce* by auto-catalysis or some bio-electric mechanism a new shape or arrangement in another component. An implanted optic cup at D induces an abdominal lens. Transplant potential tail into the head region, it transforms into head tissue. Indeed a regenerating amphibian tail placed in the eye chamber of a frog larva forms a crystalline lens.

This remarkable capacity of induction brings us to the threshold of creative behavior. The phenomenon of induction is a fundamental feature of a physiology of development and one which pervades the highest levels of organization. In his early enthusiasm, Spemann, the discoverer of the "organizer," declared, "Nature acts in development as an artist making a picture or model; indeed as every organizer does who handles materials whether living or dead."

[157]

The behavioral organism: an integrating nervous system. The higher levels of organization are attained and mediated chiefly through the nervous system. The nervous system is derived from (embryonic) neuroblasts which become neurones. Each neurone grows like a seed, but not chaotically. Metabolic gradients, potential differences, and a unifying electrodynamic field determine the primary lines and directions of growth. By the midfetal period, as we have seen, the full quota of twelve billions of neurones has already come into existence. Many of these neurones continue to grow in an embryonic manner throughout infancy, childhood, youth, and adult years.

This capacity for continued growth is more marked in the associative neurones, and in the adaptive terminals of sensory and motor neurones. It is the protoplasmic basis for the capacity to profit by experience, and to initiate new exploits. Creative behavior is made possible only through "creative acts of growth." Even the genius is dependent upon growth potentials, upon the capacity of his cortical neurones to continue an embryonic form of growth, after they have been partly organized by learned behavior. As Coghill would put it, growth *is* the creative function of the nervous system.

True genius may be defined as a creative developmental thrust of the human action system into the unknown. It arises as a unique variation in the stream of racial evolution. It achieves what was never achieved before. The thrust of genius gathers its strength, its direction, its pattern from the total past growth of the personality; that past, as we have shown, extends back to the germinal period of the ovum. And if the spiral of our inquiry swings around to the fetus, we may still be on the right track, for Coleridge himself has told us that, "the history of a man for the nine months preceding his birth would probably be far more interesting and contain events of far greater moment than all the three score and ten years that follow it."

Genius does not descend as a visitation from on high. Rather, it emerges from low levels. It is part of the order of nature. It is a rare

[158]

manifestation, but not a miracle. It has a place in the same hierarchical continuum to which less exalted phenomena belong.

According to the electrodynamic theory of life there is a reciprocal interaction between the particles of physics and surrounding fields of force which condition the behavior of the particles. A field is at once cause and effect, product and producer. Such organizing relationships are found at every level, animate and inanimate. Bio-electric phenomena underlie all physiological processes, including the complex process of growth. The electrodynamic state of a growing organism constantly changes with increasing maturity.

The growth potentials of the human nervous system are of the highest significance. The nervous system not only registers and organizes the past experience of the organism, but it brings into being new modes of reaction, in the form of attitudes, goals, insights, decisions. These creative acts are acts of growth in the sense that they depend upon the capacity of the neurones to continue an embryonic type of development. In the hierarchical continuum, creative behavior is an optimal manifestation conditioned by a morphogenetic field.

A morphogenetic field is not a mere abstraction. In nature it is an actual space-time region in which ordering forces perform morphogenetic work. Waddington's definition is apposite: "A field is a system of order such that the position taken up by unstable entities in one portion of the system bears a definite relation to the position taken up by unstable entities in other positions."

In the hierarchical continuum a system of ordering forces operates at every level of organization and supports corresponding structures. One field overrides the next below and all fields mutually influence each other. At a purely physicochemical level atoms and molecules by attraction and repulsion may produce crystals. Spatially separated small crystals may unite themselves into large ones of the same structure. Molecules can also polymerize into fibers which have crystal structure. Living systems, Needham[4] insists, actually are liquid crystals.

[4] J. Needham, *Order and Life* (New Haven, Conn., 1936). Pp. 1+175.

The crystal order is the natural expression of the properties of matter, the biological order, likewise. They are not mutually exclusive.

The distinction between living and nonliving systems thus becomes increasingly meaningless. Claude Bernard's curt definition, "Life is creation," is expanded by David L. Watson to read: "Life is a process or method, an integrally connected series of operations, an infectious principle of using stored free energy. . . . The organizing agency is not centralized as philosophers such as Rignano and Driesch imagined, but is diffused throughout the whole organism in the form of residual valence, electrostatic and electro-magnetic field patterns (static and dynamic), chemical affinities, potential differences, surface tension, absorption, and in the *speeds* with which atoms, molecules, ions, colloid particles, cells, tissues and complete organisms respond to their influences."

Under such concepts not even the most recondite mathematical symbol nor the most exalted poetic utterance can be regarded as altogether unique. Their distinction is simply that they stand at the summit of the biological hierarchy. Thought structures are just as real, just as somatic, as crystal and fiber structures. Thought structures, even those of the genius, are not singular in their anatomy or their mechanism. They are natural products. They are shaped by induction forces in the same manner that an embryonic lens is brought into being by a contiguous optic cup in a morphogenetic field. The induction forces which operate at the lofty psychical levels of creative thinking are subtle and complex, but they cannot be different in essence from those which shape the soma. Thought structures are in fact the ultra-electronic histology of the soma.

At the lowly levels of the laboratory amblystoma, the induction forces are envisaged in terms of organizing centers, evocators, metabolic gradients, time genes, and even specific chemicals. We do not of course know the intimate *modus operandi* of these agencies. Vaguely one may stereoscopically visualize a jungle of molecules with all sorts of mobile side chains interlocking and disengaging through secretly patented zipper devices under photo-electric control in a bio-electro-field system! This delicate mechanism is the product of past adjustments, and while it is a growing mechanism it remains continuously sensitive to present stimuli, alike during waking and sleeping hours. Structured thought thus becomes both product and producer, both conservator and creator.

In vital individuals the entire structure of consolidated experience has an active orientation toward the future, a striving, a driving. The drive sets up tensions which determine the general directionality of development. Laboratory experiment has demonstrated that growth takes place in the direction of maximum tension. Tension and induction are closely related concepts.

In the psychical sphere there are many forms of tension, which virtually operate like inducers and organizers. Moods and wishes exert long-range and chronic influences. Emotional events bring about acute reconfigurations; ideals and designs, intensely sustained, impose pattern on a living system of impulses and images. In the genius, the underlying repository of past experience (Coleridge's "Deep Well" and Darwin's *Note Book*) is rich and variegated. But it is the architectonics of growth governed by already structured tensions that produces the mutations of pattern and the creative syntheses which the world calls genius. In Coleridge and Melville the optimal tensions were short lived—tragically brief. In Darwin, Lincoln, and Gibbs they were steady and long sustained.

GENIUS AND CULTURE

The mechanisms of genius are biological; but the content and the criteria of genius are cultural. Giftedness is a capacity to initiate, to sustain, and to elaborate behavior which is exceptionally esteemed by the contemporary cultural group or by a later generation. We may well reserve the term genius for those rare individuals who are so supremely and uniquely gifted that they exert a permanent, significant impression on the patterns of the culture into which they were born.

This holds for all types of genius; but is most obvious in the contributions of the great men of science. Darwin, a scientist, literally transformed the intellectual and moral outlook of his age. Gibbs did not have the same wide and direct effect upon ways of thought; but his work is still profoundly affecting the important instruments of modern civilization—fuel and power engineering, metallurgy, chemical industries, cement, ores, salt deposits and fertilizers, ammonium nitrate. Ironically enough this peaceful man supplied the phase rule which in dire emergency enabled Great Britain to increase her manufacture of explosives in the First World War. His influence continues in the present war of metals and demolition.

All of which leads us to a final and sobering reflection. Society must find new devices for making optimal use of its geniuses. We can only hope that Gibbs's contribution to the study of living as well as non-living systems will ultimately lead to a better understanding and control of human forces. Even genius must be brought under social control. It depends on biological genetics and chemical energetics, but it functions in a social order.

PART THREE

Clinical and Social Applications

The Changing Status
of the Preschool Child*

Twenty years ago this journal opened its pages to a discussion of the then very new nursery-school movement. (Dr. Charles W. Eliot at that time was honorary president of the Progressive Education Association; H. G. Wells was vice-president.) The writer contributed a brief article on "The Changing Status of the Preschool Child." The conclusion to that article may now be quoted by way of preface.

"In Law, in school practice, in home life, in public health provisions, in the clinic and in the laboratory we see a new trend in the times. That the journal *Progressive Education* should so promptly dedicate a whole number to the problems of preschool education is itself an auspicious sign."

In the space of twenty years the status of the preschool child has continued to change. We are beginning to see him in truer social perspective. It was once suggested that the kindergarten would meet the challenge of the times; would reconstruct and readapt its methods to embrace the earlier age levels. But when the Great Depression came, the kindergartens of America were curtailed; over a hundred cities closed their kindergartens and many made drastic reductions.

The ensuing Federal Emergency Education Program shifted public

* Part of a Symposium printed in *Progressive Education*, February 1946, pp. 132 ff.

interest to the nursery school; and in the mid-1930's some 3000 nursery school units, employing 7,500 persons and serving 65,000 needy children, were organized. Under the urgency of World War II, preschool child-care centers and nursery-school units were multiplied on a vast scale. The public, including some school administrators, have become increasingly aware of the educational significance of the preschool period. And it has been suggested that the nursery school should be made an integral part of our public-school system, tax supported, with attendance privileges extended to all the children of the nation. The shades of Plato and of Robert Owen stir in sympathy.

Does not this envisagement, however, oversimplify the status of the preschool child? He may be suffering from educational want, but he has other basic needs. From the standpoint of broad public policy these other needs must also have basic consideration.

The welfare of the preschool child begins with birth, and indeed with gestation. Measures for his protection involve the fundamental fields of maternity and infant hygiene. This was recognized in principle by the U. S. Congress as early as 1921, in the passage of the Sheppard-Towner Act which made federal funds available for the medical care of mothers and babies. Again with the urgency of war this health program was greatly expanded. Under the Emergency Maternal and Infant Care section of the Social Security Act, the Children's Bureau makes grants to public-health agencies to enable states to extend and improve maternal and child-health services. During 1943 over 145,000 mothers received prenatal care under this program; some 450,000 infants and preschool children attended medical child-health conferences; over 1,000,000 received public-health nursing service.

The supervision of infant nutrition, both in health centers and in private practice, is steadily expanding to include mental as well as physical welfare. This leads to individualized, periodic contacts with the growing child. His behavior characteristics, his psychological maturity, and hygiene are then taken into account. With the increase of scientific knowledge the protection of child health evolves into a form of developmental supervision.

Recognizing this trend, The American Academy of Pediatrics has made the field of Growth and Development one of its major requirements for certification. The importance of more facilities for the training of pediatricians and general practitioners in the field of mental health was recently stressed in a "Report of Committee on a Consideration of Child Health in the Postwar Period." Through this report the Academy has taken a position which in the estimate of its official journal has "the potentiality of becoming the most forward-looking step in the development of sound child health activities for the future that has been made in years." The problems of child health have been formulated "in a way which can fit into any program which may evolve for medicine in the postwar United States."[1]

The administrative organization of that program cannot, of course, be predicted. But many surveys and projections have been made which indicate the needs and the trends of a more co-ordinated health service for the nation. Especially notable are the findings of the United States Senate Committee on Education and Labor. The Interim Report of its Subcommittee on Wartime Health and Education urges an integrated system of health services with health centers in every community to combine preventive, diagnostic, and curative care. Four basic types of facilities are proposed: the small neighborhood or community health center, the rural hospital, the district hospital, and finally, the large base hospital, with constant exchange between these units of information, training, consultation service, and personnel.

President Truman's comprehensive message on national health, November 19th, 1945, was an arresting statement of the needs of more equitable care at all ages of the life cycle. The message outlined a five-

[1] The American Academy of Pediatrics is now completing a Study of Child Health Services which is unique in origin and scope. The profession, with the help of federal and private funds amounting to over $1,000,000, has on its own initiative undertaken a survey to determine concretely the extent of present medical care, the role of general practitioners, pediatricians, and specialists in relation to child care. An evaluation of the needs of pediatric education points to an increasing emphasis on mental as well as physical health.

This notable study had its inception in 1944 when the academy committed itself "to make available to all mothers and children in the United States of America, all essential preventive, diagnostic and curative medical services of high quality which, used in cooperation with other services for children, will make this country an ideal place for children to grow into responsible citizens."

[167]

point program for a comprehensive coverage of the 3,000 counties of our nation.

We are not here concerned with the financial and governmental aspects of such a vast program. The proposals, however, have brought into focus the kind of arrangements necessary for a more fundamental child-health protection. This protection must be consecutive and individualized rather than piecemeal; it should be based on a periodic, and so far as possible, a personalized supervision. Otherwise we cannot get at the preventive roots of mental abnormality—the maladjustments of child life and family life.

An adequate health plan would include well babies and would set up more nearly universal safeguards against preventable disease, against malnutrition, and against maternal and infant mortality. In rural areas less than half of all births take place in hospitals. Each year some 200,000 babies are born without medical care for either mother or child. Two out of every three rural counties have no well-baby clinics where mothers can bring their babies for check-up and advice. A thousand counties have no public-health nurses to help mothers with their child-care problems. It is evident that a nursery-school movement largely confined to urban communities would not meet the needs of large sections of our population.

There seems to be no device by which the public-school system can reach these areas of need and neglect. It is possible, however, to project an organic program, basically medical, which will be directed toward the joint conservation of physical and mental health, which will be oriented to the child as a member of the family group, which will incorporate parental guidance, and flexible educational provisions for preschool children, adapted to all types of communities.

An organic program will of necessity follow the natural course of the life cycle, which moves in forward direction from gestation through infancy and childhood. A complete system of developmental supervision will begin with an anticipatory mental hygiene of the expectant parents, and with the birth of the infant. It will follow his development at significant intervals to ascertain the assets and liabilities of his growth make-up. For social reasons it will have regard for the positive potentialities as well as for deficits and abnormalities of growth. For the social welfare it will be directed toward detecting and conserving what is distinctive and superior in the individual infant and pre-school child.

This recognition of the factor of individuality would save a system of developmental supervision from the dangers of totalitarian regimentation. With this factor of safety we can confidently undertake a system of developmental supervision, democratic in scope and designed to increase the mental welfare of the nation by protecting the mental growth of the first fundamental years of life.

Only through a democratically conceived system of developmental supervision can we attain a more just and universal distribution of developmental opportunity for infants and preschool children. If, in the period of postwar reconstruction, first things are, in fact made first, we shall approach all problems of child conservation with a chastened outlook.

Let us hope that Vice-President H. G. Wells is wrong when in his literary testament he suggests that the human mind is at the end of its tether.

A Guidance Program for the Handicapped Preschool Child[*]

This is a notable conference. It is, in fact, the first of its kind in the history of child welfare. Under a comprehensive, pioneering statute, the great state of Illinois is bringing the handicapped child of preschool age officially within the scope of public policy. All educable, handicapped children from 3 to 21 years of age are now entitled to special educational services and facilities under the administrative regulations of the Office of the Superintendent of Public Instruction. During the current biennium, over 30,000 such children in public-school districts have benefited from state reimbursement appropriations amounting to seven and a half million dollars. The Illinois Plan which is taking shape is bound to erect standards and to have leadership influence upon the country at large. There is no contingent in our child population more in need of systematic public assistance than the scattered army of handicapped infants and preschool children.

Handicaps vary enormously with respect to origin, severity, and effects upon the personality of the growing child. Inheritance, disease, and injury may damage or distort the normal course of development in four different areas: sense perception, motor performance, intel-

* Read at the Conference on Special Education, Auspices of the State Office of Public Instruction, Chicago, Illinois, November 21, 1947.

ligence, and conduct. Sometimes more than one area is affected in the selfsame child. To appreciate the nature of a handicap, it is well to have a concrete knowledge of the characteristics of normality. Such knowledge will give sympathetic insight into the disadvantages under which the handicapped child suffers. To understand the needs of the blind child, we must know how seeing develops in the sighted child. To be patient with the deaf child, we must know what speech means to normal social experience. To sense the frustration of the spastic and palsied child, we must consider the mechanisms of unencumbered motion. To adapt to the retarded child, one must think of him in terms of his maturity rather than his age and size.

Our task, however, is not to make him over into an intact child. That cannot be done. The goal is to have him realize to a maximum the potentialities of *his* development. The handicapped child is thrice handicapped if society fails to give opportunity for his growth potentials.

The handicaps of infancy and childhood are extremely individual. They do not yield readily to group approach. Each child must first be considered in terms of his unique needs, his own family, and his own life career. Infancy, the preschool years, and the school and vocational years are part of a single sequence. Looking at the general problem in broad perspective, it is obvious that the first five years of life are of basic importance. They are of critical significance when we consider the four major phases of control which apply to all types of handicap: 1. Registration, 2. Diagnosis, 3. Guidance and Therapy, 4. Special educational services.

1. REGISTRATION

In some way, society must discover and identify the handicapped children who will benefit most from a co-ordinated program—a program which ideally should begin with birth rather than at the age of 3 years. A compulsory form of registration would not seem to be the best solution. The registration should come, so far as possible, through the spontaneous demands of the parents for medical, social, and educational services. There are many families who feel that a handicapped child stigmatizes them. They tend to conceal their problem. Sometimes they labor under the gross misconception that their own child with motor disabilities and wild arm movements must be "crazy," when in truth he is not mentally abnormal. Many a parent is obsessed by obscure doubts and misgivings, which could be dispelled by authoritative interpretation. What is needed is a more general diffusion of information concerning the nature and origin of handicaps, and the educability of the handicapped. This can be accomplished by methods of adult education, and of civic education at high-school and junior-college levels. In this way citizens are made aware of the resources of their community and they may learn to acquire more intelligent attitudes toward the handicapped individual. The evolution of the Illinois Plan will be hastened by a broad program of public enlightenment, which reaches both professional and lay groups. This may also hasten needed legislation in other states.

2. DIAGNOSIS

Practically every case of handicap in infancy and childhood comes first of all to the attention of the physician, either as pediatrician, or as the family doctor. This fact has far-reaching implications for public policy and planning. Timely and accurate diagnosis proves to be the very foundation of an adequate program of guidance, therapy, and education.

Every evidence and every suspicion of handicap, be it "physical" or "mental," is charged with deep emotional reactions for the anxious parent. On first impact these reactions may be overwhelming and carry mixed feelings of guilt, rejection, dismay, despair, and accusation. To the doctor, the parents turn for help. Immediately or step by step, he must arrive at a diagnosis and interpret the diagnosis. He will be asked more questions than he can answer, but none that he can evade. The realization of the handicap may come suddenly or by slow degrees. Whether the handicap concerns sense perception, motor performance, intelligence, or personality factors, the physician will have to appraise the integrity and the organization of the child's action system as manifested in behavior capacities. These capacities can be assessed by functional behavior tests with the aid of maturity norms. Intelligent parents will demand a thorough examination by a conscientious and interested physician.

Some handicaps are relatively obvious and require no special diagnostic techniques. It is, nevertheless, amazing how often visual defects, deafness, and marked retardation are overlooked when the child's physique is relatively normal in appearance. An ordinary neurological examination may fail to disclose minimal cerebral injuries which produce personality deviations. Timely diagnosis of minor yet consequential defects requires a detailed developmental examination, exploring all fields of behavior—sensorimotor, adaptive, language, and personal-social. Whatever the nature of the handicap, the diagnosis should be imparted in a constructive manner, with candor, yet with great consideration for the grief-stricken feelings of the parents. This taxes the professional skill of the physician. His task is to interpret the diagnosis in such a way that the parents will be intelligently oriented to their problem. They are particularly concerned to know what effects the handicap will have on the course of the child's development. Overprecise predictions can be avoided. The supervising physician will see the child from time to time, and will interpret the handicap in terms of the child's progress. Developmental diagnosis, developmental supervision, guidance, and therapy are inseparably interrelated.

3. Guidance and Therapy

Medical oversight is needed from the beginning to give direction and stability to a systematic guidance program throughout all of the five preschool years. In due course, the public-health nurse, social worker, home visitors, and special teachers will share in an expanding program, which however should always remain individualized by the particular handicap of an individual child. The modern pediatrician is interested in the behavior aspects of development, and he will be increasingly interested when it is recognized that the educational welfare of the handicapped child begins in infancy, long before he becomes of school-going age.

Consider briefly the early developmental and educational needs of several types of handicap.

The Blind Child. If the handicap is restricted (and often it is not) to the visual mechanisms, the blind child is highly educable. He may grow into a useful or even a gifted adult. Blindness per se does not produce a serious degree of retardation. In relatively normal sequence, the blind infant will show a tendency to hold up his head, to grasp and manipulate objects, to creep, to stand, to walk, to explore his environment by action and by words. But he needs much more than ordinary help. Early he erects his head even though he has nothing to look at. It is the first sign of the urge to sit up and take notice. If the urge is unrewarded he will too readily remain content lying in his crib. His parents also may be too content to let him lie. He should be propped with pillows from time to time so that even at this early age he may exercise behavior patterns natural to his maturity level. He can take hold of the world with his hands if not with his eyes.

Even more fully he must be admitted into the personal world, which consists of parents, brothers, sisters, playmates. They must touch this infant with affectionate hands, so he will not feel alone. They must talk to him unceasingly so that he will remain in contact with them. Otherwise he will be wrapped in a fog of personal isolation which is much more handicapping than mere darkness. He must not be allowed to withdraw into himself, or to be content with stereotyped, repetitive forms of play.

By the age of 3 and even earlier, he can profit from nursery-school experience in a small group of sighted children of similar maturity. But

[174]

the consistencies and the intimacies of home life are so important to his total psychological welfare that too much reliance can not be placed on institutionalized, group education.

The Deaf Child. Socialization, likewise, is the first essential in the care of the deaf child. He too shows a tendency to retreat into himself when a two-way socializing communication is not set up. Early diagnosis would help parents to understand the necessity of abundant communication by gesture, by facial expressions, by visible signs, and pantomime. If the handicap is not recognized either by parent or physician, the deaf but otherwise normal child, is poignantly frustrated by his inability to communicate and to comprehend. He flares into explosions due to his self-vexation: he bursts into tantrums. He may even be punished for obstinacy and disobedience. But once his condition is understood by his family, the whole situation tends to clear up. He becomes less irritable, less "suspicious," less puzzled, less confused. He begins to give more attention to persons; he is not so intensely preoccupied with things. He is less vehement in voice and manner. Even his nutrition may show improvement with his calmer emotional organization.

Parents of the deaf child sometimes give too much attention to the deafness and too little attention to the growing child himself. The child must learn to live with his handicap. When he is mature enough he can be taught many useful things. He may even learn to speak to a gratifying degree. But while he is an infant and young child, there should not be an excessive emphasis on early lip reading on the mistaken assumption that the earlier the better. A late start is usually better than an ill-advised premature start. Early communication is so important to the child's personality and his ultimate capacity to lip read and to talk, that one should welcome any kind of language which he may wish to use, even if he talks with exclamations, grunts, gestures, and dramatic motions. An intelligent parent does not have to be a specialist in order to give the young deaf child the right kind of experience. But the parent may benefit very greatly from well-planned

[175]

direction. In the treatment of preschool handicaps, much child guidance must come through parent guidance.

The Mentally Retarded Child. The first step in the guidance of the mentally retarded child is accomplished when the parents accept the diagnosis of retardation. This diagnosis must be imparted by the physician. He helps the parents to understand that the child's behavior is conditioned by his maturity level and capacity for further growth. They must recognize that the child is not backward from mere lack of teaching. Misguided efforts at early training beyond his maturity level are harmful. If the child is 4 years old and his developmental level is 2½ years, he must be treated as a 2½-year-old.

The guidance program for the retarded child must be individualized in terms of the family welfare and the ultimate vocational outlook. In the more severe degrees of retardation, the parents may be gradually induced to look ahead and foresee the positive benefits of institutional placement. These benefits should be pointed out by emphasizing their medical and educational advantages. Parents should be discouraged from sacrificing too much for a defective child at the expense of the welfare needs of brothers and sisters. In the milder cases of mental retardation, a relatively optimistic outlook is justified, and even during the preschool period parents may be encouraged to realize that the child as he grows up can acquire some vocational or occupational skills which will make him a useful member of society with simple safeguards and supervision.

The Cerebral Palsied Child. No handicap is more in need of intelligent understanding than cerebral palsy. No handicap takes as many variegated forms. At one extreme, we have the devastated type in which all growth potentials are abolished. This type cannot come under the auspices of a Department of Special Education. At the other extreme the handicap is minimal. It may even escape notice in infancy and yet it can be discovered by methods of developmental diagnosis which bring the deviating behavior patterns into view. Atypical motor signs show themselves in inco-ordination of eye movements, in sucking, swallowing, and other feeding reactions, in reaching, in hand, arm, and finger postures, in delays and deformations of speech. Sometimes, also, there are deficits in vision and in personality organization.

Between the two extreme types lies a vast group of selective cerebral palsies in which the motor disabilities may be moderate or severe. They may be so severe as to suggest that the child is mentally deficient. But again discriminating developmental diagnosis of behavior may reveal a relatively normal intelligence and personality. The motor disabilities manifest themselves in the fields of prehension, manipulation, locomotion, speech, and emotional control. Just as blindness and deafness are sensory handicaps, so spasticity and athetosis are essentially motor handicaps. The symptoms are extremely diverse, and for this reason each case requires careful and periodic diagnostic study. In this type of handicap, a careful explanation of the meaning of the symptoms is especially important. Such explanations will help the parents to understand the nature of the handicap, the purpose of the training, the rationale of the orthopedic measures. A palsied child is not a sick child, but a crippled child. He does not need overprotection. He needs understanding and opportunity suited to his disabilities. But he cannot get such understanding unless parents are enlightened through interpretive guidance.

A complete program for the preschool handicapped would include provisions for the speech defective, the undervitalized and physically defective, and various types of maladjusted and unstable children. The general principles of guidance and therapy apply with modification to all of these various types of handicapped. During the preschool years the child guidance and parent guidance are very closely related to each other and the supervision should be directed chiefly to the psychological factors involved in the parent-child relationship.

4. Special Educational Services

When the problem of the handicapped preschool child is envisaged in its home setting, it becomes clear that all educational services must be primarily directed to the parents and to the household. The psychology of the preschool child, whether handicapped or not, is rooted in the home. His emotional life, particularly his sense of security, is bound up with the family circle.

Special educational services, therefore, must generally take the form of advisory counseling with parents and caretakers, group meetings of parents, home visits by educational and guidance workers, planned demonstrations, individualized correspondence-course contacts, radio, pamphlets, and other forms of dissemination. By ingenious planning a small group of highly trained experts can diffuse its influence widely, reaching even remote rural areas and villages. Fortunately there are many private and quasi-public agencies already in the field, whose assistance can be enlisted. So many people are eager to help that sometimes duplicating independent approaches must be avoided. Administratively it seems desirable to build up programs on an individualized basis, beginning wherever possible with the physician who in private or other capacity is responsible for the medical welfare of the infant. Educational services can be mediated through him as well as through the parents.

The limitations of nursery schools for the handicapped are apparent. In sparsely settled districts, the nursery school is impracticable. Since the psychology of the preschool child is so deeply rooted in his home life, there is a real hazard in the residential type of nursery school. The dangers of institutionalization are everpresent if the child is separated from his parents. A daytime nursery group, however, operated as an adjunct to the home may promote the socialization of the handicapped child; for this child returns regularly to the securities and the attachments of his home. Such a nursery group can be conducted as a guidance center with individualized attention directed to the parents quite as much as to the child. Informal nursery groups may be extremely valuable but such groups should not be conducted so much as training schools or treatment centers, but as experience centers. Often their value will prove greatest for the parents. The parents profit by associating with each other and by observing more objectively the problems of child care as they arise in children not their own. It is, of course, possible to plan educational conferences and discussion sessions for groups of parents independently of the groups planned for the children themselves.

SUMMARY

In terms of long-range planning an adequate guidance program for the preschool handicapped would have to achieve a fair balance between medical, educational, and social controls. The essentials of a comprehensive program may be summarized in a series of statements somewhat as follows:

1. Early medical diagnosis and periodic medical supervision are basic.

2. This diagnosis properly includes a developmental examination of the behavior capacities of the child and a progressive, periodic appraisal of his developmental potentialities.

3. Initial guidance and orientation should be supplied by the supervising physician. He is in the best position to impart the diagnosis constructively and to interpret its implications.

4. During the first 3 years of the child's life, the responsible physician translates his interpretations into actual guidance and co-ordinates his supervision with the forthcoming educational services.

5. Under co-operative and anticipatory arrangements, these educational services may make preparatory contacts with the family prior to the age of 3.

6. Broadly interpreted, educational services include a wide variety of activities: a) home visitation for parent counseling; b) home teaching periods and demonstrations by an educational field worker; c) small informal preschool groups for children to supply social experience; d) similar groups of parents for conference, discussion, and mutual exchange of experiences; e) special institutes for parents and workers; f) flexible guidance nursery centers designed both for children and for parents.

7. A state-wide program needs continuous adult education, not only for the parents, but for the public at large, for the private social welfare agencies, for government departments and for various lay and professional groups, including regular as well as special teachers.

8. The over-all planning should encourage an integration of the three main sectors of a continuous program, namely: 1) the infant years; 2) the preschool years; 3) the school years. These three sectors can be made to articulate with each other and the foundational importance of the first 3 years of life should be consistently recognized.

Under a state-wide program there is a lessened danger that the handicapped child will be concealed and isolated. For this reason, the state program should be widely publicized so that the citizens of the state will have pride and a sense of participation in the program. In Illinois, this will indeed be a justifiable pride. Having taken the initial pioneering step it is in your power to erect standards and goals for the benefit of handicapped children throughout our country.

CHAPTER XVI

A Method of Developmental Diagnosis and Supervision[*]

Every generation must rediscover and re-evaluate the meaning of infancy and childhood. The present cultural crisis is thrusting our social problems into new perspective. First things, we may hope, will come more nearly first. There is every prospect that the protection of child development will be increased and enriched in the period of post-war reconstruction.

How can that protection be achieved? Not only through good will, nor by symbolic concepts of good and evil, but by a deepened insight into the laws and the nature of early child development. Every newborn infant comes into the world endowed with growth potentialities, which are the essence of his individuality. To understand any child, whether normal or handicapped, we must understand his ways of growth.

And what are the ways of growth? They are physical, and they are also functional. First and foremost, we are concerned with sheer bodily growth, measured by inches, ounces, and pounds. But this leads to a concern for the physiological functions of metabolism, elimination, circulation, biochemical susceptibilities and immunities; fatigability, vitality; motor co-ordination; feeding habits; sphincter control; vision;

[*] Characteristic of British spirit under war conditions was a letter received from the Editor of *Nursing Times*, London. The letter requested an article describing the Yale method of developmental diagnosis. The present chapter is a reprint of that article (March 4, 1944).

hearing; speech; perception; capacity to profit by experience, and readiness to conform to the mores of the home and the community.

All these functions are inextricably interrelated because the child is a unity and because he grows as a unit. Development defies dualism: it is a single, all-embracing process governed by profound laws. As such, it falls within the scope of preventive and supervisory medicine. Clinical pediatrics, in particular, will be increasingly concerned with a comprehensive protection of child development—a protection which will include psychological as well as bodily welfare. Needless to say, the profession of nursing has a stake in all these impending extensions of psychosomatic medicine into the vast field of child protection.

Such are the underlying general principles. The practical consequences are concrete enough. The periodic health examination of infants and young children should be broadened to include behavior characteristics. Behavior is the most comprehensive index of a child's maturity and well-being. Behavior assumes patterns which can be objectively tested and observed. These patterns change with age; they can be clinically diagnosed. *Developmental diagnosis is a diagnosis of maturity status. Specifically, the developmental diagnosis of infants is the application of graded functional tests of behavior to determine the maturity and the integrity of the central nervous system. Such tests are significant for all types of children, normal as well as defective and handicapped.*

BEHAVIOR PATTERNS AND BEHAVIOR FORMS

The body grows; behavior grows. The infant is a growing action system. He comes by his mind in the same way in which he comes by his body—that is, through processes of development which create maturing patterns of behavior. Biologically considered, his mind indeed is a complex of growing behavior patterns.

In our method of developmental diagnosis, we use very simple objects to elicit characteristic patterns of behavior—patterns which are symptomatic of stages and degrees of maturity. For example, one of our test objects is a red, one-inch cube. The newborn infant is so immature that he cannot perceive the cube, but he does clasp it with a reflex grasp when it is pressed into his palm. At 16 weeks, when the infant is held in a supported sitting position, he perceives a nearby cube and fixates his eyes upon it. His nervous system is growing at a prodigious rate.

At 24 weeks, he can co-ordinate eyes and hands: he seizes a cube on sight. It is a crude palmar grasp. At 28 weeks, the radial digits come more prominently into play. New behavior patterns are taking shape as the nervous system undergoes its progressive organization. Having seized a cube, he can, at 28 weeks, shift it by transfer from one hand to another. At 40 weeks he grasps the cube deftly by thumb opposition. At 12 months he can release the cube on intent. At 18 months, he builds a vertical tower of three cubes. At 2 years, he builds a horizontal wall of three cubes, at 3 years a bridge of three cubes, and at 5 years he builds a staircase of six cubes, et cetera.

These are lawful sequences of growth, only secondarily influenced by cultural factors. They are so fundamentally determined by intrinsic growth factors that they may be used as criteria for appraising the maturity and integrity of the nervous system. All psychological development, even in the sphere of intelligence and emotions, is subject to similar maturity sequences. *These growth sequences and these patterns of behavior are identified and appraised through the method of developmental diagnosis.* There is no peculiar mystery in the formal examination of an infant's behavior patterns or in the evaluation of these patterns with the aid of diagnostic behavior norms. Development is made accessible to diagnosis through a normative method of behavior appraisal.

The method is based upon a systematic investigation of the behavior growth of a large group of normal infants whose development was followed at periodic intervals from birth through the first 5 years. The infants were examined under controlled but homelike conditions with the full co-operation of the parents. Great care was taken to secure natural and optimal behavior. Extensive cinema records were made at lunar-month intervals during the first year of life and at lengthening intervals later. These records were subjected to minute inspection, and analyzed as so many anatomical cross sections of behavior patterns. The home behavior of the infants also was explored. On the basis of these periodic observations, it was possible to define the behavior characteristics typical of a series of advancing age levels: 4, 16, 28, and 40 weeks; 12, 18 months; 2, 3, 4, 5 years.

Four major fields of behavior were embodied in these norms of development as follows:

(1) *Motor behavior:* posture and locomotion; prehension and manipulation; gross and fine motor co-ordination.

(2) *Adaptive behavior:* self-initiated and induced behavior; learning; resourcefulness in adjusting to new situations; exploitive behavior.

(3) *Language behavior:* vocalizations; vocal signs; words; gestures; comprehension.

(4) *Personal social behavior:* reactions to persons; response to gesture and speech; socialized learning; habits of self help.

Typical or normative behavior traits were codified in the form of developmental schedules, embracing the first 5 years of life. One of these schedules is illustrated on the facing page.

THE DIAGNOSIS OF INFANT BEHAVIOR

For diagnostic purposes, the behavior tests are administered in accordance with standardized procedure. The infant's behavior characteristics are recorded on the developmental schedules. A critical appraisal of the various behaviors makes it possible for an experienced examiner to derive a descriptive estimate of the child's maturity status in terms of his age. We hasten to point out that this is not a psychometric intelligence test which is numerically and mechanically scored. No effort

GESELL DEVELOPMENTAL SCHEDULES

NAME	AGE	DATE	CASE No.

24 Weeks	KEY AGE 28 Weeks	32 Weeks
MOTOR		
Su: lifts legs high in ext.	Su: lifts head (40w)	Sit: 1 min., erect, unsteady (36w)
Su: rolls to prone	Sit: briefly, leans fwd. (on hands) (32w)	St: maintains briefly, hands held (36w)
P. Sit: lifts head, assists (40w)	Sit: erect momentarily	Pr: pivots (40w)
Sit. Chair: trunk erect (36w)	St: large fraction of weight (36w)	Pellet: radial raking (36w)
Cube: grasps, palmarwise (36w)	St: bounces actively (32w)	Pellet: unsuccessful inferior scissors grasp (36w)
Ra: retains	Cube: radial palmar grasp (36w)	
	Pellet: rakes (whole hand), contacts (*32w)	
ADAPTIVE		
D. Ring, Ra, Cube, Bell: approaches and grasps	Ra, Bell: 1 hand approach and grasp	Cube: grasps 2nd cube
Ra: prehen. pursuit dropped Ra	M. Cubes: holds 1, grasps another	Cube: retains 2 as 3rd presented
Cube: regards 3rd cube immediately	Cube: holds 2 more than momentarily	Cube: holds 2 prolongedly
Cube, Bell: to mouth (18m)	Bell: bangs (40w)	Cup-cu: holds cube, regards cup
Cube: resecures dropped cube	Ra: shakes definitely	Ring-str: secures ring
M. Cubes: holds 1, approaches another	D. Ring, Cube: transfers	
	Bell: transfers adeptly	
	Bell: retains	
LANGUAGE		
Bell: turns head to bell	Vo: m-m-m (crying) (40w)	Vo: single syllable as da, ba, ka
Vo: grunts, growls (36w)	Vo: polysyllabic vowel sounds (36w)	
Vo: spontan. vocal. social (incl. toys)		
PERSONAL-SOCIAL		
So: discriminates strangers	Feeding: takes solids well	Play: bites, chews toys (18m)
Play: grasps foot (supine) (36w)	Play: with feet to mouth (supine) (36w)	Play: reaches persistently for toys out of reach (40w)
Play: sits propped 30 min. (40w)	Mirror: reaches, pats image	
Mirror: smiles and vocalizes	Ring-str: fusses or abandons effort (32w)	Ring-str: persistent

Developmental Schedule: listing diagnostic behavior norms for the 24 weeks, 28 weeks, and 32 weeks levels of maturity. Reading across these schedules permits comparison in the four major fields of behavior: motor, adaptive, language, personal-social behavior. Reading down a single column affords a thumbnail behavior profile for a specific age level.

is made to derive an intelligence quotient or I.Q. An interpretive estimate of intelligence can be made, but the aim of a developmental examination is to appraise the total developmental status in terms of the four major fields of behavior. The diagnosis is expressed in a descriptive statement rather than a numerical value. The method is clinical and pediatric, and should obviously be distinguished from psychoanalytic procedures. It is an objective method which can be applied even to infants of tender age. It is, as already suggested, essentially a pediatric form of clinical neurology, and requires special training in the details of technique.

The practical arrangements and physical equipment for the developmental examination are simple in principle. They are indicated by the illustrations in Chapter II (p. 31). An ordinary hospital crib with adjustable side panels can be converted into a clinical crib for the conduct of the developmental examination. Examinations are made with the infant in supine, prone, and standing position, or seated before the test table top which spans the crib. A washable, canvas-covered chair with supportive band is a serviceable device for the younger infants.

In a hospital or teaching center the examination unit should have a separate locus and should function as a special diagnostic department. Systematic training in the application of the techniques and actual diagnosis requires one or two postgraduate years on a fulltime service.

The actual examination procedures cannot, of course, be detailed in a brief article. They are described at length in various publications, particularly in a volume on *Developmental Diagnosis*,[1] designed for students and practitioners of medicine. Although the procedures in themselves are relatively simple, skilled interpretation of the results of the behavior tests requires clinical experience. The type of developmental examination here described can be incorporated as a clinical tool both into private practice and public health supervision.

[1] Gesell, A. and Amatruda, C. S. *Developmental Diagnosis: Normal and Abnormal Child Development.* P. B. Hoeber Inc., N. Y. (Second Edition, Revised and Enlarged, 1947. 496 pp.).

A METHOD OF DEVELOPMENTAL DIAGNOSIS AND SUPERVISION

THE CLINICAL PROTECTION OF CHILD DEVELOPMENT

If, in the period of postwar reconstruction, first things are in fact made first, we shall approach all problems of infant and child welfare with a broadened and a chastened outlook. We shall take more seriously the status of the newborn baby, as an individual, whose personality is fundamentally shaped in the first formative years of life. This personality cannot be adequately protected merely through improved nutrition and the correction of physical defects. The total complex of development must be safeguarded. This can be accomplished only by medical and public health measures which will take into account the behavior make-up of the individual infant from the time of birth.

Development does not take care of itself. In a complicated society, it needs to be subjected to periodic diagnosis and supervision. Otherwise we shall not discover the defects and deviations of development in their early stages. And the great mass of parents of "normal" children will lack the guidance necessary for understanding the nature and needs of early development.

Timely diagnosis of maldevelopment depends upon routine developmental examinations of infant behavior. Through the application of behavior tests, nearly all cases of mental deficiency (amentia) can be recognized in the first year of life. Instabilities and emotional abnormalities also declare themselves early, when diagnosis is directed to the appraisal of maturity. The examination of behavior serves to disclose sensory defects in vision and hearing, and motor disabilities which might otherwise escape detection. Such an examination is essential to a discriminating differential diagnosis of selective cerebral injury and amentia. Cerebral birth injuries frequently simulate amentia, and children with motor defects are often mistakenly classified as mentally deficient. Developmental diagnosis reveals normal and constructive features as well as shortcomings in an infant's behavior equipment. A discriminating insight into behavior potentialities is essential to any intelligent program of guidance and treatment. All handicaps need interpretation in terms of their developmental significance.

These considerations apply with equal force to "normal" and privileged children. Every child has a distinctive pattern of growth, which needs as much understanding as we can bring to bear. In this task of understanding and rearing children aright, parents need assistance from the very beginning. Nursery schools are useful educational agencies when they are organized as guidance centers for the enlightenment of parents.[2] But nursery establishments as such, do not solve the basic social problems of child protection. We need clinical provisions for diagnosis and supervision which reach down into the period of infancy, and which focus upon mental as well as physical welfare.

In the long run, and in last analysis, we cannot rely only upon improved political and economic conditions to reconstruct the social order of a postwar world. We must rely upon a better understanding and control of the human units, the individuals who constitute the community. Infants are individuals.

Full recognition of the factor of individuality will save a socialized system of developmental supervision from the dangers of totalitarian regimentation. With this factor of safety we can confidently undertake a system of developmental supervision democratic in scope and designed to increase the mental welfare of the nation by protecting the mental growth of the first fundamental years of life.

In the religious outlook of the Middle Ages, something of the meaning of birth and infancy was captured. In these later scientific ages, our task seems to be to recapture that meaning, to bring it to higher issues in a culture which by protecting the beginnings of life may yet avoid another apocalypse of violence.

[2] For a discussion of the nursery school as a guidance center, see Gesell and Ilg: *Infant and Child in the Culture of Today.* New York and London. Harper & Brothers, 1943, p. 399.

The Differential Diagnosis
of Developmental Defects

THE IMPORTANCE OF EARLY INTERPRETIVE DIAGNOSIS

Because mental deficiency is vaguely regarded as a "hopeless" condition, there is a regrettable tendency to minimize the importance of diagnosis and of supervision. The problem, however, cannot be evaded. It arises in many different forms and in unsuspected guises. It also causes such extreme anxiety and suffering on the part of parents that it becomes a challenge to medical skill and judgment.

Mental deficiency is not the type of problem that can be conveniently referred to a specialist. Practically all the cases come first of all to the attention of the pediatrician or of the general practitioner. He is in a strategic position to make a timely diagnosis, and also to make a progressive diagnosis, coupled with interpretive, constructive guidance.

Practically every case of mental deficiency can be diagnosed in the first year of life, excluding, of course, the small number of exceptional cases which occur from secondary causes in later infancy or early childhood. This does not mean that all cases become obvious in the first year or two. A large proportion remain ambiguous, confusing, or positively misleading unless subjected to careful differential diagnosis.

Without such diagnosis, there are three possible consequences: (1)

a defective child may be called normal; (2) a normal child may be called defective; (3) the case may be dismissed with vague optimism: "He will outgrow it!" None of these consequences is desirable.

To be sure, there are not a few cases which are so complicated that the physician must use great caution. He may have to make two or three examinations at spaced intervals. He may even have to resort to a therapeutic test, if environmental handicaps are present. He should not rely on intuition, on casual inspection, or even on physical stigmata. Progressive appraisal of the child's maturity status from time to time will permit him to impart an unfavorable diagnosis guardedly and gradually. By such a policy only can false optimism and bitter disappointment be avoided.

It is the physician's duty to help the parents to face reality as early and as steadily as possible. This cannot be done by exploding an adverse diagnosis, with bombshell abruptness. The physician may have to awaken misgivings first. When the parents begin to ask questions spontaneously as a result of such misgivings the way opens to frank discussion.

Mental deficiency—or amentia, to use a more convenient term—assumes many and protean forms. The standard designations, idiot, imbecile, and moron, are not much more than classificatory labels. They have no value in imparting a diagnosis. The "diagnosis" should be an interpretation of the condition in terms which the parents will understand. Once convinced, they will want to know why and how it happened to them, what the child will be like when he grows older, and whether they can have other children.

These questions, as we have indicated elsewhere,[1] have to be answered as wisely and as kindly as possible. They have to be answered on the basis of real knowledge and actual possibilities rather than guesswork. This means interpretive rather than classificatory diagnosis. The physician may need to call the parents' attention to important questions which they do not think to ask: What about the effect of this child

[1] Gesell, A., and C. S. Amatruda: "Developmental Diagnosis and Supervision," *Brennemann's Practice of Pediatrics*, Volume I, Chapter IX.

on themselves and on their other children? These effects can reach psychiatric proportions. The entire family welfare is involved. Finally, the parents will ask what is to be done.

DIAGNOSIS AND PROGNOSIS

Every diagnosis of mental deficiency carries by implication a prognosis, because by definition mental deficiency (amentia or feeble-mindedness) is a state of development so generally defective from birth or infancy, that the individual will never be able to shift for himself in a self-dependent manner. A diagnosis of mental deficiency in infancy should not be made if the child in question has potentialities which may enable him as an adult to adapt himself adequately to community life.

The first task of differential diagnosis, therefore, is to make this broad distinction between normality and defectiveness—a distinction which is both biologic and medico-legal. The ultimate criterion is *behavior.* Will the future adult have capacity for *adaptive and social behavior* sufficiently mature to conduct his affairs with ordinary prudence? In the presence of the problematic infant or young child we ask an equivalent question. How has he (the infant) met the demands of past development? How is he now meeting the normal tasks of life? Does he show adequate command of his body postures, supine, prone, sitting, standing? Can he roll, creep, walk, run? Does he show discriminative regard for sights and sounds? Does he reach for, grasp, manipulate, and release objects? Does he exploit and has he exploited his environment in a varied and increasingly elaborate manner? Does he show a propensity to learn and to profit by experience? Does he communicate with his social environment by visual following, by intent regard, by smiles, by gesture, vocalizations, and words? Does he react discriminatively to persons? Does he show a normal capacity to assimilate the culture into which he was born?

This last question is in many ways the most crucial in all cases requiring differential diagnosis. It has far-reaching implications with respect to the child's developmental potentialities. If, throughout the first year of infancy, he fails to meet the ordinary expectations of the household; if his adaptive behavior, his language, and his personal-social adjustments are consistently retarded or reduced, it is quite likely that he will be similarly inadequate in the years of maturity. A normal infant is one who can meet the tests of life and growth. An ament cannot.

There are three major degrees of amentia: idiocy, imbecility, moronism. The differential diagnosis between these three degrees is not of much technical importance. Prognostically speaking, an idiot will have no vocational capacity whatever; he will not even be able to guard himself against ordinary physical dangers. His development is so slow and incomplete that he will remain at a more or less helpless infantile level. The imbecile can in time learn a few routine tasks and the simplest forms of self-care. His adult behavior capacities will range roughly from the 3-year to the 7-year level. The moron attains capacities ranging from 7 to 11 years. He can be trained to routine work, but will need protective oversight. He cannot plan adequately for himself. The foregoing differences are almost too broad to have much clinical significance, but it is important to recognize and to define the train-ability of the higher grades of mental deficiency. These long-range forecasts, however, must be taken into approximate account when establishing a diagnosis in infancy. Parents will need long-range as well as close-range orientation. The physician's task is to help them, stage by stage, to see the problem in full perspective, in terms of the future life cycle.

The tendency of all development, whether normal or abnormal, is toward an optimal realization. This principle is of importance in developmental prognosis. It has added force when the infant's original endowment is superior. He may have suffered a cerebral injury, but superior endowment serves to protect in some measure his residual potentials.

THE DIFFERENTIAL DIAGNOSIS OF DEVELOPMENTAL DEFECTS

THE BASIS OF DIAGNOSIS

The diagnosis of amentia rests on three methods: (1) medical history; (2) physical examination; (3) developmental examination of behavior. In differential diagnosis these methods assume a variable importance, depending on the nature of the problematic condition; but the third method remains the court of final and most inclusive jurisdiction. Behavior appraisal is the most fundamental approach because it is the most direct. Our objective is to determine the potentialities of development by identifying the end products of development. We do this by means of functional tests of behavior, because the infant's patterns of behavior are the most immediate, the most complete, and the most profound indicators of his developmental maturity. An infant is as old as his behavior.

We appraise behavior in terms of age norms. We define developmental age in terms of behavior patterns. We therefore evaluate the integrity and the maturity of the infant's nervous system by a series of systematic reaction tests[2] designed to disclose the four basic fields of behavior: (1) motor; (2) adaptive; (3) language; (4) personal-social behavior. For purposes of differential diagnosis as we shall see, it is especially important to give separate as well as conjoint consideration to each of the four major fields of behavior. In typical amentia, of a primary (intrinsic) variety, all four fields are somewhat symmetrically retarded and reduced. In secondary (acquired) amentia, there are inequalities among the several fields. In simulated cases there may be profound arrest and impairment in the motor and language fields, with relative normality in adaptive insight and personal-social attitudes. Interpretive diagnosis always demands specific formulation of the developmental outlook in *each* of the four fields.

For this reason it is impossible to rest a diagnosis on a so-called intelligence test or an I.Q. determination. The I.Q. is the ratio between

[2] A full account of the procedures and clinical applications is set forth in Gesell, A., and C. S. Amatruda: *Developmental Diagnosis: Normal and Abnormal Child Development*, New York City, Paul B. Hoeber, Inc. (Second Edition, Revised and Enlarged, 1947. Pp. 496.)

[193]

intelligence age and actual age expressed in percentage (16 years being regarded as the equivalent of an adult level). A ratio of $3:4 = $ I.Q. 75 is presumed to mark the borderline between normality and amentia. An I.Q. 100 represents a normal average. For clinical purposes such a psychometric rating is an oversimplification. The D.Q. on the other hand, is more discriminating. It is the ratio between the maturity age and actual age. The D.Q. can be specifically ascertained for each separate field of behavior and for individual behavior traits. It can therefore be used analytically and with qualifying reserve. Even the D.Q. needs clinical interpretation. The behavior picture must be interpreted as a whole and in the light of the child's growth career.

The *medical history*, accordingly, is particularly concerned with the behavior biography of the child. The behavior interview, like the examination, explores all four fields of behavior as far as possible by concretely directed questions. The history also considers the etiologic factors which may operate at five different epochs in the early life cycle: the germinal period, the embryonic, the fetal, the circumnatal, and the postnatal. Developmental potentials are reduced by germinal defects and by a host of extrinsic, mechanical, traumatic, toxic, infectious, biochemical, environmental, and personal-social factors. All differential diagnosis must estimate probabilities as well as certainties. Probabilities can be weighted by estimating etiologic factors. Often, however, etiology remains obscure.

Physical examination is directed chiefly toward the discovery of somatic stigmata, anomalies, and neurologic abnormalities. In mongolism, cretinism, microcephaly, and hydrocephaly, the physical signs may be so characteristic and well defined as to establish a secure basis for a diagnosis. However, these types have a way of defying the textbooks, and they are themselves subject to many variations which lead to error and confusion. Infants who look mongoloid not infrequently prove to be normal. Infants who look unquestionably normal prove to be defective. If the doctor is psychoallergic to an epicanthic fold, he may overreact with an erroneous diagnosis. Moreover, a diagnosis on the basis of physical stigmata gives us only a little more than a classificatory label. An interpretive diagnosis demands an investigation of the concealed anatomy of the central nervous system which makes itself manifest only in the patterns and modes of behavior.

Even when the precise technics of electro-encephalography and of pneumo-encephalography are employed to penetrate the status of the brain, we are nevertheless finally thrown back upon the evidences of behavior. A pneumo-encephalogram may give a picture of cerebral atrophy; but the developmental examination of the child's behavior may reveal no abnormality. The behavior picture then supersedes the testimony of the X-ray.

In *differential diagnosis*, it is, of course, desirable to secure evidence from every possible source. Whenever this evidence seems contradictory or inconsistent, most reliance must be placed upon the behavior symptoms, for these sum up most conclusively the trends and the effectiveness (or defectiveness) of the organism. This broad principle is of great importance in establishing a difficult diagnosis. One may be tempted to give undue weight to some physical stigma which catches the eye, or to some single event in the past history, or to an over-conspicuous feature in the child's adjustment. It is the total behavior picture which needs judicious appraisement. And one must recall that amentia in all its forms, contexts, and complications is an extremely diversified condition. Oftentimes it does not only need a differential diagnosis; it calls for multiple diagnoses.

We shall now list some of the actual clinical situations in which these issues come to concrete expression.

Amentia and Cerebral Palsy

Devastating Injury. Apart from primary, germinal defects, the brain may be injured before, during, or after birth by trauma, hemorrhage, infections, toxins, and anoxemia. The injury may be so devastating as to produce profound idiocy. The deficiency soon becomes obvious.

Countenance and physique, however, remain unblemished and may create a misleading impression of normality in early infancy.

Example. An infant 2 weeks old. His eyes rove, he smiles; but neither reaction is related to an outside stimulus. His "adaptive" behavior is almost restricted to feeding and respiration. He shows no interest in objects or persons. He makes no prehensory approach on a dangling ring, enticingly brought near his eyes and hands.

Selective Injury. An injury may seem devastating but may actually be selective. Here an accurate differential diagnosis becomes of extreme importance. A distinction must be made between a severe lesion and a devastating one. A lesion can be so severe as to produce a profound motor disability which simulates idiocy. Yet the lesion is frequently confined to the basal ganglia, leaving the cortical structures intact. If the child's original endowment was normal or superior, his developmental potentialities survive. They express themselves in strivings, emotional attitudes, and insight, even when speech fails.

Example. A 40-week-old boy was so disabled motorwise from a birth injury that he could not sit up without support. Arms, trunk, and legs were spastic. Voluntary movements were performed with fantastic distortions. But they were performed with remarkable vigor and eagerness. He managed to grasp a rattle and bring it momentarily to his mouth. His interest and drive were unmistakable. Adaptive behavior was at a 24-week level—a serious degree of retardation: 24 weeks:40 weeks = D.Q. 60. Ordinarily such a low D.Q. means amentia. Careless diagnosis classifies such infants erroneously as feeble minded. Differential diagnosis recognizes their underlying psychological normality and developmental assets. Subsequent examinations over a period of years have demonstrated the favorable prognostic import of the behavior signs observed in infancy. Paraplegia persists; speech is spastic; but at the age of 8 years, he is learning to read with notable success; and even to use a typewriter.

Minimal injuries are observable in infancy, but tend to resolve with age in children of good endowment. The concealed injury manifests itself in overactivity, in slight retardations and deviations of postural control and manual co-ordination, in exaggerated startle reflexes, emotional sensitivities, and articulation difficulties. Obscure personality peculiarities are sometimes attributable to such minimal injury. Intelligence is usually unimpaired. They illustrate the rule that birth history is of highly variable and sometimes of temporary significance in differential diagnosis.

Example. An infant girl, age 34 weeks. She showed slight retardation in postural control; sitting was of the narrow base adductor type. Deep reflexes were hyperactive; left arm weak. She overreached on grasping; she overextended on release; her thumb opposition was atypical and suggestive of a neurologic impairment. Her facial expression was at times alert, at times blanked out, suggestive of weakness of facial muscles.

The birth history was astounding: quadruple fracture of parietal and occipital bones; head contused; bleeding from the ears. Apathy, listlessness, flaccidity, and sensitiveness to handling lasted a whole month. On the basis of birth history this child might well have been diagnosed as a low-grade idiot; but even at 34 weeks her behavior patterns were at a full average level of maturity. At the age of 1 year, she was a big, healthy, happy, vocal infant, deliberate, poised, and self-controlled. Behavior is the court of last resort.

Example. Contrast an infant boy, in whom the birth history was altogether negative. At one year he showed signs of cerebral damage in strabismus, marked ocular inco-ordination, weakness of upper trunk, and atypical hand-arm-finger patterns. Environment was unsatisfactory; outlook doubtful. Behavior showed an extremely wide scatter in maturity levels from 8 to 40 weeks; but a diagnosis of amentia was restrained. The neuromotor defects, though exacerbated by environmental factors have proved to be of a resolving type. Slight residuals remained at the age of 6 years; but the behavior picture has undergone radical amelioration and reorganization. Although the birth history was quite negative, this boy undoubtedly suffered a cerebral injury. Several examinations were necessary to establish the seriousness and the permanence of the damage inferred on the basis of behavior signs.

AMENTIA AND ENVIRONMENTAL RETARDATION

Developmental retardation is the cardinal symptom of amentia. The retardation may become evident in the first weeks of life; it is almost always present after the first few months, when cortical controls normally assume ascendancy over subcortical. The retardation denotes a reduction of intrinsic growth potentialities, it is permanent, it may even increase. The growth curve either flattens or decelerates prior

[197]

to physical maturity. In true amentia the biologic equipment for behavior has suffered curtailment.

There is another type of developmental retardation, which is more benign in the sense that it is comparatively impermanent. It is due to paucity of environment rather than paucity of biologic equipment. It responds to environmental therapy. It is therefore of extraordinary importance in individual cases. It requires acute differential diagnosis.

Here the developmental history is often of decisive significance. The history warns against a snap diagnosis. If the child has had early and more or less prolonged institutionalization, behavior output is depressed. The behavior may become so meager, so withdrawn (because withheld), and so narrowly channelized as to suggest serious retardation. The retardation is serious, but it is remediable. Excessive hospitalization, impoverishing institutionalization, or injudicious hypersanitary neglect in an oversophisticated family home, produce this characteristic syndrome.

Example. Diminished interest and reactivity and reduced integration of behavior may begin as early as 8 or 12 weeks. Excessive preoccupation with strange persons, blandness of facial expression, ineptness in social situations, debilitated initiative, exaggerated resistance to novelty and slowness in speech—all become manifest and intensified in children of inferior endowment or sensitive temperament. At 28 weeks an institutional baby may prefer to lie on his back; he indulges inordinately in hand inspection, head rolling, head nodding. His patterns congeal into blind-alley stereotypes. They cauliflower whereas normally they would differentiate, elaborate, and grow. A timely therapeutic test (removal into a family home environment with radiating pathways instead of blind alleys) will release the impeded growth potentials. In doubtful cases such a test may be necessary to establish a differential diagnosis. The "amentia," that is to say the retardation, is truly symptomatic: it disappears when the causative factors are removed.

Amentia and Pseudo-symptomatic Retardation

There is another type of retardation which is falsely ascribed to environmental factors, and turns out to be a true amentia. The most persistent and elaborate therapeutic tests prove of no avail. The diagnosis of amentia, however, usually comes late or is strongly resisted if it comes early. The parents (and sometimes the physician also) consider the child to be frustrated or "blocked" rather than mentally deficient. The child to them seems oblivious rather than dull. They see a wistfulness in the pauses which punctuate his bizarre behavior. They see "concentration" in the narrowing of his attention. They magnify the apparently normal aspects of his conduct: "He does some things so well"; "He is a good boy"; "He seems unhappy"; "Something is holding him back."

In these cases accurate diagnosis is delayed because wishful fixations on the part of the parents, the normal appearance of the child, and the very "strangeness" of the behavior, conspire to perpetuate an uncritical optimism even in the face of contradictory evidence. In many instances the bizarre behavior patterns are due to an encephalitis. Development is *both* retarded and disorganized. There are no removable causes. If the child were only retarded, the diagnosis and its acceptance would come earlier.

Example. A small, active, appealing child at 3½ years of age was almost completely heedless of persons. Yet he showed brief flashes of attention. He would look for brief moments at a picture book, with apparent concentration. The mother firmly believed that except for inattention to words, he was like a normal child, and that forcible feeding had set up an emotional blocking. He did not walk until the age of 27 months. The significance of this simple retardation was overlooked. The seriousness of the associated behavior was underestimated. This behavior included aimless running, snatches of hand regard, tongue sucking, clicking, blowing, rubbing of the abdomen, etc. In the search for psychogenic factors, a psychiatric interpretation may delay the recognition of a frank amentia.

AMENTIA AND PREMATURITY

Prematurity of birth constitutes an abnormal alteration of environment which might conceivably affect the developmental career of the infant. The effects are adverse if through hemorrhage or otherwise the cerebrum is injured. In the absence of complications, however, prematurity of birth in itself does not markedly distort, hasten, or delay the course of development. Instead it results in a fictitious form of retardation, which vanishes as soon as the chronologic age of the child is corrected by subtracting the amount of prematurity. The retardation is an artifact.

Example. Baby C was examined at the age of 24 weeks. She needed considerable support to maintain the sitting position. In supine decubitus she took notice of near objects. She promptly perceived a dangling ring. She followed it 180° as it was moved across the field of vision. She did not prehend the ring, but she brought her hands to the midline over the chest, and engaged in mutual fingering. She held a rattle placed in her hand and regarded it. She assumed the tonic-neck-reflex attitude from time to time.

By all these tokens she was at a 16-weeks level of behavior maturity: $16:24 = $ D.Q. 65. On the face of it, this is a serious degree of retardation. But the child was born 8 weeks prematurely. She is really only 16 weeks old, discounting for the birth displacement: $16:16 = $ D.Q. 100. She satisfies a full average expectation. The developmental prognosis is entirely normal. If prematurity is not taken into account, an erroneous diagnosis of retardation or of amentia may be inflicted.

Amentia and Sensory Deprivation

Vision and hearing are so important for the patterning of infant behavior, that blindness and deafness have a retarding effect on the rate and the fullness of development. If the handicap is limited to the receptor mechanisms, this retardation may be regarded as symptomatic. Through systematic educational devices, the handicap is, at least, compensated for. The child ultimately reaches a level of relative maturity and comparative self-dependence.

But in the first 3 years of life, he may be so seriously retarded (on the basis of ordinary behavior norms), and he may be so seriously misunderstood that he occasions a diagnosis of amentia. Sometimes even the deafness escapes recognition. It is astounding how often deafness in a young child is overlooked (even by the physician) because of a preoccupation with the peculiar, aggressive, or withdrawn aspects of the child's behavior. Here the detection of the etiologic factor is of prime importance.

THE DIFFERENTIAL DIAGNOSIS OF DEVELOPMENTAL DEFECTS

Blindness and deafness occur more frequently among aments than among the normal population. Prognosis must, therefore, be guarded. If the sensory handicap is a complication of a more extensive pathology, the outlook is poor. Sensory education will not promote more normal development. If, however, the sensory defect is a specific disability, early diagnosis and suitable management in the preschool years will have a profoundly beneficial effect on personality organization and mental growth.

Example. An infant 4 weeks old presents an atypical behavior picture. He lifts his head high in prone position; he retracts his head when supine. He gives regard to a dangling ring after delay and follows it from left to right through an arc of 180°. He startles to sounds. His hands are loosely open. The anterior fontanel is almost closed. The child is obviously not normal, but a diagnosis cannot be defined.

The same infant at 20 weeks gives no visual regard to the dangling ring and does not respond to light. He is now hypertonic and spastic both in arms and legs. He does not attend to sounds or voice. He is active, takes solids well; he has a specious "alertness" due to the tonicity of his facial muscles and the roving activity of his eyes. The conformation of his head is more nearly normal but the fontanels are closed. The diagnosis is amentia of severe grade, with degenerative, sclerotic changes. The blindness is a complication and not an etiologic factor.

Example. Infant B, on the contrary, presented a relatively normal behavior picture at 20 weeks. His ocular responses were alert. His eyes followed a moving person; they picked up a tiny pellet placed on a table surface well within the infant's visual field. He gave such full notice to what was happening around him that he was regarded as quite normal.

But as he grew older, he showed a certain indifference to sounds and to the spoken word. He played vigorously (and intelligently) with toy objects, but paid less attention to persons. He reacted to noises; but did not co-operate in the nursery games. Sometimes he seemed puzzled and unhappy for no reason at all, or even when one tried to make friends with him. He remained silent or vocalized in a monotonal way; he ceased to laugh (as he used to). He enjoyed tokens of affection; but after he learned to walk he often displayed violent tantrums. He did not learn to talk at all. You could not reason with him. As time went on he was regarded as a very backward and a very difficult child.

Finally someone made the bright discovery that he was deaf! He was not mentally deficient after all.

[201]

MONGOLISM AND CRETINISM

These two conditions have received much attention in the medical literature, partly because they are well-defined clinical entities, evidenced in characteristic physical stigmata and signs. Nevertheless, they often escape early diagnosis and are even confused with each other. Differential diagnosis rests on the following distinctions. Mongolism arises in utero, possibly from germinal factors, though the etiology is unknown, and can be diagnosed at birth even in the prematurely born infant. Cretinism usually declares itself some weeks after birth. Stature is stunted in both conditions; uniformly in the mongol; more especially in the legs of the cretin. The head is smallish and flattened at the occiput and temples in the mongol. It is more shapely in the cretin, though the brow is low and wrinkled and the jaw prognathic. The eye slits in the mongol are disposed outward and upward; in the cretin they are horizontal. The skin of the mongol is smooth in infancy and not dry, scaly, or flabby as in the cretin. Tapered, short fingers and a wide space between great toe and next toe are characteristic of the mongol. It is the composite of all these physical traits which is distinguishing.

Behavior traits are equally distinctive. The mongol may be inert but usually he is lively; the cretin is bland and apathetic. The young mongol grimaces and snorts in his activity, displays fragments of plausible behavior; is affectionate, cheerful, imitative. Progressive retardation is the rule. The rate of growth becomes very slow by the age of 5 years, and declines to a developmental quotient of 50 or less.

The cretin may also show progressive retardation; but this is at least partly overcome by thyroid therapy. Mongolism does not respond to thyroid feeding. Thyroid feeding may be properly used as a differential therapeutic test, but not as a placebo. Physical improvement occurs invariably in the cretin on thyroid treatment. An equal degree of mental improvement occurs in only a few favorable cases.

The physical signs of cretinism appear gradually in early infancy, and should be discerned long before they cumulatively create their classic composite.

Example. Cretin 36A had a very wide anterior fontanel at birth; the skin was observed to be pasty and mottled at 2 weeks; the abdomen was protuberant by 3 weeks; subnormal temperature, dwarfism, umbilical hernia, sluggishness, and behavior retardation were noted by the second month. Infiltrative signs became more evident by the fourth month. The lids thickened; hair was dry and coarse, voice hoarse. Diagnosis was possible long before the infiltrative signs reached their culmination in a textbook facies.

Mongol A. B., on the other hand, was diagnosed as such immediately after birth, even though born prematurely. When his head was viewed in profile, it presented a characteristic conformation, supported by other physical signs. The diagnosis held even though the behavior patterns, themselves, in the early weeks simulated normality.

AMENTIA AND EPILEPSY

The differential and parallel diagnosis of amentia and epilepsy in infancy is a subject of great complexity. Infantile convulsions vary enormously in gravity and also in etiology. It is virtually impossible to detect epilepsy in early infancy, since chronicity or recurrence constitute a diagnostic criterion. Electro-encephalography is not yet decisive as to epilepsy; and pneumo-encephalography may be actually misleading.

In cerebral degenerative disease, on the other hand, the pneumo-encephalogram consistently shows cortical atrophy and ventricular dilatation. The birth history and neonatal development are usually normal; subsequently the behavior undergoes progressive deterioration.

Example. Infant girl, age 41 weeks, smiled, laughed, rolled, and even "reached" for toys in the early months. Regression began after the fourth month, with 14 convulsions prior to the ninth month followed by a mild but chronic convulsive state. The pneumo-encephalogram pictured marked ventricular dilatation and cortical atrophy. Diagnosis: cerebral degenerative disease.

Example. Contrast infant girl, age 15 months. The pneumo-encephalogram similarly showed bilateral cortical atrophy. The birth history and early development were again normal. At one year generalized convulsions began, at first several daily and then about twice per week. The developmental examination of behavior, however, showed performance and maturity well within the normal range. The child was bright and alert; displayed no motor weakness, walked with support. She built a tower of two cubes, inserted a pellet into a bottle, imitated a scribble, gave a toy to the examiner on verbal request.

The follow-up on this child justifies an additional note. At 20 months convulsions continued at weekly frequency; but the behavior maturity level was 18 months. At 27 months, convulsions became infrequent. Behavior development continued normally. At 43 months only one convulsion was reported for the previous year. Behavior had risen to a high average level.

CONCLUSIONS

This last case will serve as a final illustration of our main thesis, namely, that a differential diagnosis of developmental status must rest upon an orderly examination of behavior. Such an examination defines the function and the integrity of the nervous system. It also indicates, when complicating factors are duly recognized, the capacities for future development. In the presence of normal behavior, as shown by a study of a series of epileptic cases,[3] pneumo-encephalographic evidence of cortical atrophy is prognostically meaningless. Behavior is the final criterion both for diagnosis and prognosis.

In conclusion, we would repeat our emphasis of the importance of interpretive diagnosis. Accurate diagnosis is the most fundamental essential. Mental hygiene measures and child guidance efforts are pointless and even harmful if they do not rest upon sound diagnosis. In fact, the primary responsibility of the physician is to make a considered diagnosis and then to interpret the implications of that diagnosis constructively to the parent. This looks like a truism, but it demands repetition because under the pressure of parents and social workers there is a real danger that even the hardheaded pediatrician will embark upon mental hygiene and guidance programs which put the cart before the horse because they are not supported by adequate diagnosis. Diagnosis remains the essential work horse.

[3] Amatruda, C. S., "Pneumoencephalography and the Developmental Diagnosis of Behavior." *Journal of Pediatrics*, 21:147-179, August 1942.

STUDIES IN CHILD DEVELOPMENT

outstandingly concerned with the diagnosis and supervision of child development, normal and abnormal.

THE HYGIENE OF DEVELOPMENT

Development is a very usable concept, both for theoretical and for...

to both mind and... involves the laboratorians of psyche and soma...

it also helps to... between... and...

environment, between... normal and abnormal, between structure and function. Development is an integrating concept. In fact, it is a development which keeps the child from falling ever under the disruptive stress of excessive medical specialization.

Every newborn child carries an invisible, conspicuous cargo of...

CHAPTER XVIII

Developmental Pediatrics: Its Task and Possibilities*

In 1933 the American Board of Pediatrics set up the field of Growth and Development as a basic requirement for specialty certification. When the medical history of the twentieth century is written, we may be sure that this formal action of the board will be regarded as a uniquely important event in the evolution of clinical medicine. Already we can see that a clinical science of development is in the making, and that the hygiene of the growing child is being envisaged in the dynamics of his growth. (We shall use the terms growth and development interchangeably for they are virtually synonymous.) Health is a somewhat static idea, unless by health we mean that condition which promotes optimal development.

Pediatrics is distinctive among all the specialties in three ways:

1. It is a specialty of general medicine.
2. It is directed to an age sector of life, rather than to an organ system.
3. It is basically interested in normality as well as disease.

Developmental Pediatrics is a form of clinical medicine which is

* Read at Sixteenth Annual Meeting of the American Academy of Pediatrics, Dallas, Texas, December 10, 1947.

systematically concerned with the diagnosis and supervision of child development, normal and abnormal.

THE DOCTRINE OF DEVELOPMENT

Development is a very usable concept, both for theoretical and for practical purposes. It is a unifying concept. It applies with equal force to body and mind. It resolves the false dualisms of psyche and soma. It also helps to resolve artificial distinctions between heredity and environment; between normal and abnormal; between structure and function. Development is an integrating concept. In fact, it is development which keeps the child from falling apart under the disrupting stress of excessive medical specialization.

Every newborn child traverses an indivisible, continuous cycle of growth. And for that very reason, the child remains the most cohesive force for the maintenance of family life in our democratic culture. The practicing pediatrician instinctively thinks of the child not only as the end product of aeons of evolution, but also as a most important member of a family group; and by the way, also the citizen of the future.

The cycle of child development begins with pregnancy. Biologically speaking, the cycle continues into the third decade of life. It embraces infancy, childhood, and youth. But from the standpoint of preventive and supervisory pediatrics, the first five years are of supreme, over-shadowing significance. It is in this area that society is demanding a concentration of medical and social safeguards.

Responsive to this deep-seated demand, the pediatrician and the general practitioner are becoming increasingly concerned with the prenatal as well as the early postnatal period of development. The developmental welfare, the nutrition, and to some extent even the immunization control of the infant-to-be begins before birth. A wise and benevolent obstetrician will freely grant that the pediatrician has a legitimate role in that part of maternal hygiene which is preparatory to parenthood. The psychological orientation of the mother, and also the father, to the problems of the neonatal period can be anticipated by suggestive guidance in the prenatal period. This guidance should not be assigned to some auxiliary specialty, but should be part of a continuous pediatric policy of developmental supervision.

First and foremost, the postnatal supervision will focus on nutrition and the biochemical status of the organism. But the regulation of nutrition, even at a physiological level, inevitably leads to a diagnostic interest in the behavior characteristics of the infant—what he does, when he does it, and how he does it constitutes a symptomatology. For the physician the behavior patterns of the infant are symptoms: to the parent they furnish clews and cues for intelligent child care. Behavior is the baby's language. He expresses himself in cries, and quiescence, in squirmings, in bodily attitudes, in facial tensions, in mouthings, in hand posturings, and eye movements. Spontaneous behavior thus becomes an indicator of his current well-being and his immediate needs.

But not all of his needs are immediate. From month to month he moves onward through a cycle of growth. His long-range needs must be considered in terms of that long-range cycle. This is the task of developmental pediatrics, as a branch of clinical medicine which is systematically concerned with the diagnosis and the supervision of child development.

From the standpoint of clinical science, development is a process which yields to objective methods of investigation. It can be observed, measured, and appraised in three major manifestations: (a) anatomic, (b) physiologic, (c) behavioral. Psychosomatically no sharp distinction can be made between these three manifestations. The interaction of physical and mental factors is recognized. But if the mind as well as the body falls within the scope of pediatric medicine, chief attention must be given to the behavior patterns of the infant. His behavior characteristics constitute the most comprehensive index of his developmental status and of his developmental potentials.

[207]

THE FUNCTIONS OF A DEVELOPMENTAL EXAMINATION

Fortunately, the developmental examination of infant behavior can be undertaken with relatively simple techniques. Using the plain appurtenances of a crib, a table surface, and a series of simple, toylike test objects, it is possible, in a fraction of an hour, to elicit a rich array of behavior patterns which reveal the organization and the integrity of the child's total action system. The behavior examination is conducted formally, with precision of purpose.

In clinically experienced hands it serves five functions as follows:

1. It ascertains stages of maturity and rates of development in all types of infants, normal, subnormal, atypical, superior.
2. It yields differential diagnoses in relation to normality, amentia, and specific developmental deficits and deviations.
3. It brings to light otherwise concealed neurological defects and sensory impairments.
4. It renders objective information as to emotional and personality traits of the infant, and throws light on parent-child relationships.
5. It implements a periodic type of developmental supervision.

These several functions represent an almost unoccupied area of preventive medicine. Can clinical pediatrics take over this vast domain?

Can it possibly do otherwise? From historical necessity the pediatric profession already holds the most strategic position in the whole scheme of medicine—it is situated at the portals of birth. It is medically responsible for the welfare of the newborn infant and his continuing growth. To the pediatrician, as specialist, or as general practitioner, gravitate all the emotionally charged problems which concern the hygiene of early child development—the feeding problems of the normal infant with all their ramifications; the parent-child relationships; the gnawing anxieties if the child develops too slowly, or exhibits strange behaviors; the vague dread based on illnesses, disabling disease, physical defects, and traumatic injury, blindness, deafness, convulsive disorders, endocrine dysfunctions, congenital anomalies, and the varied cerebral palsies, devastating, selective, and mild; and for good measure, the child born out of wedlock. All these problems have a cultural and a family setting; and whether the child be normal or otherwise, the guardians of the child instinctively turn to the doctor for initial guidance and orientation. In one form or another all these problems involve the diagnosis and the medical supervision of early child development.

DEVELOPMENTAL SUPERVISION AND CHILD PSYCHIATRY

The demands for such supervision will grow more intense with the increasing intelligence of the public, and with the elaboration of health services already under way. The progress of the life sciences which deal with the biochemistry, the biophysics, the physiology, and the pathology of growth will lead to more systematic protection of infant development. The world-wide study of cancer as a form of atypical growth, and the brilliant researches of experimental embryology, will almost certainly yield important knowledge for the control of normal organic growth. With new knowledge there will be refinement of techniques, and we may hope that the techniques can be applied with improvement rather than loss of human values.

The period of infancy is the primary responsibility of Pediatrics. The child, to be sure, develops into the period of adolescence; but the professional status of clinical pediatrics would be strengthened by a concentration on the first years of life, and may be weakened by a dispersion over the entire growth span.

The present task of Developmental Pediatrics is clear enough: its possibilities, likewise, are so clear that one is tempted to paint the future with Utopian colors. It is difficult to see how any other branch of clinical medicine is in a position, in itself or as a co-ordinator, to take over the vast work of mental hygiene implicit in the pediatric supervision of infants and young children. Pediatrics is a type of general medicine, and as such it includes psychosomatic medicine. Its theory and principles are rooted in the biological sciences. It is oriented to utilize their progressive discoveries with a minimum of ideology. Developmental Pediatrics, therefore, can bring into being a new type of child psychiatry, with a realistic, integrative approach upon the dynamics of growth. The mental hygiene of infancy must of necessity reckon with the laws and mechanisms of development. *Developmental methods of diagnosis and supervision constitute the basis of a workable infant psychiatry.*

A Developmental Unit for Postgraduate Training

These desirable possibilities can not be realized overnight, but they can be hastened through a few changes in the arrangements of medical education. And what I venture now to say, is, with due qualification, addressed to the younger men who are going to shape the pediatrics of the future.

For sake of argument, I shall assume that development as well as disease and that mind as well as body fall within the scope of clinical pediatrics. Our view of the mind is downright monistic. The child comes by his mind in the same way that he comes by his body, namely, through orderly processes of growth. Accordingly, mental and physical welfare are indivisible, each reacting upon the other.

One may also assume that the private pediatric practitioner, or his equivalent in a diagnostic team, will be highly cognizant of the child not only as a biological organism, but as a personality whose psychic structure is profoundly influenced by the cultural pattern of the home and the mores of the community.

On these premises the education of the general and of the developmental pediatrician will give great weight to the genetic aspects of science which interpret the evolutionary origins of man and his nature as infant, child, and adult. A broadened embryology might well become a key science, dealing in a co-ordinated way with the morphogenesis of embryo and fetus, the developmental anatomy of infant and child, the physiology of the fetus, the developmental chemistry of infancy, with special reference to maturity changes in allergy and metabolism, the biometry of bodily states in relation to maturity factors, the developmental aspects of physical anthropology. All this somatic knowledge can be brought into correlation with the embryology of behavior, the ontogenetic patterning of physiological and psychological functions— the patterning of autonomic reactions, and the growing forms of motor, adaptive, and personal-social behavior. Body types, psychic-constitution types, maturity and age norms, may be organized into normative criteria as aids to diagnosis. A clinical condensation of cultural anthropology would illuminate the status of the child as a member of the human family.

Such a program of professional training can be anticipated at undergraduate levels. It would come to an apex in a hospital training center, where the intern and resident would have one or two years of intimate participation in a diagnostic and guidance service dealing with the whole gamut of developmental problems in their human context. Postgraduate training should also take him into varied child-care institutions and into the homes of the handicapped children, so that he will be confronted with the manifold personal and social implications of the problems.

This type of set-up envisages a functional diagnostic unit, with a separate locus for developmental examinations and facilities for the naturalistic observation of infants and preschool children. An adaptable therapeutic and guidance service for parent and child could be used to refine the prognosis and the recommendations. Emphasis would be placed on systematic follow-up study in order to individualize the care of handicapped and defective children. A periodic health service for normal infants, with intensive developmental surveys at a few selected age levels, would be part of a well-rounded developmental unit.

Under the auspices of such a unit the physician in training can be inducted into the art as well as the science of medicine. He will be compelled to understand the parents as well as the child, to detect their hopes, fears, beliefs, and mental conflicts. He will interpret the needs of the child in relation to this complex of personal attitudes, and he will apply his psychological insight in imparting diagnosis and advice. Thereby he acquires skill in the art of medicine; and also receives an education in social and moral responsibilities.

The program outlined is not impractical. In spite of its wide coverage it permits the simplification which comes with correlation and synthesis. The integrational potency of the concept of development will in itself consolidate rather than multiply the burdens laid on the physician in training.

THE OUTLOOK

If the progress of civilization is not halted, the social demands for health services in the first years of life will increase in volume and penetration. The growth of the nursery-school movement, the downward extension of the public-school system, the expansion of parent education, show the trend of the times.

The instability of marital relations is ominous, but the zeal with which parents pursue the physician for advice in the rearing of the young indicates the latent strength of the family. There is, moreover, a rising feeling that the usual well-baby conference has reached a plateau of subefficiency, and that it should be vitalized and transformed into a more powerful educational agency. This could be done by incorporating a higher level of developmental diagnosis and supervision.

The almost systematic social neglect of the handicapped preschool child is too well known. One state, however, Illinois, has recently set aside millions of dollars to reimburse local districts for the special education of their exceptional children. In a noteworthy pioneering statute, this state responsibility has now been extended downward to the age of 3 years, to provide educational services for all types of preschool handicapped children—the blind, the deaf, the crippled, the speech defective, the retarded, the undervitalized, and the maladjusted.

We mention this legislation because it draws aside a curtain and brings into view the crucial years before 3 when the family and society inevitably turn to the physician for instruction in child care, for guidance, and for wisdom. These years are too critical and emotionally too complex to be entrusted to agents and agencies not conversant with the deep human and medical issues which are involved. The physician remains the pivotal professional person in this sector of life. Here lies the challenge and the task. To young men the vista opens upon far-reaching possibilities.

The Cultural Significance of a Science of Child Development

On the fourth day of February 1864, the very month in which he called for 500,000 volunteers, Abraham Lincoln formulated a remarkable sentence in behalf of a widowed mother who sought his help. He wrote this sentence in his own clear hand on the back of a folded letter:

> If oath shall be made by this lady & the gentleman accompanying her that she is a widow with four small children, & no person to assist her unless it be the son in the Army, let that son be discharged.
>
> A. Lincoln

Here we have a poignant reminder of the inescapable problems of child care which confront a nation at war; and by similar token, a nation at peace. For the wartime needs of children are the needs of peacetime. Children always require food and shelter, affection and protection, understanding and guidance. These three kinds of need, physical, personal, developmental are so profoundly joined that there is only one institution in our culture which can fully satisfy them. That institution is the home.

We are now in a cultural crisis because the very goals for which two world wars were waged remain in jeopardy. The United Nations has written into the Great Charter a determination "to reaffirm the dignity and worth of the human person." This sweeping proposition applies to children no less than to adults and it can not be fully applied without preserving the integrity of home life.

Every infant has the right to be born in wedlock and to have the nurture which a good household provides. Each newborn infant has a distinctive growth potential and a pattern of growth unique to him as an individual. This pattern is so intrinsic that it can not be transcended with impunity. The spirit of liberty has its deepmost roots in the biological impulsion toward optimal growth. A democratic way of life alone can respect this impulsion in children and channelize it into social responsibilities.

These axioms enhance the cultural significance of a science of child development. We need a broadened science to define and to refine our system of values with regard to marriage, procreation, education, and the everyday art of living. Such science cannot be contained in an ivory tower. It must permeate the homes of the people, reshape the attitudes and interpersonal relations of the family unit, and of the local community; for a community is a collection of families. In application this kind of science will give new dignity and importance to the task of rearing children. It will inevitably reshape our overinstitutionalized arrangements of elementary education and liberalize our methods at secondary and college levels. At these levels there promises to be a type of preparental education concretely based on a science of child development.

The life sciences become new humanities when they are socially utilized to interpret the nature and the needs of early human growth. The culture of tomorrow will be dependent in no small measure upon a deeper insight into the dynamics of human behavior. Symbolic concepts which rigidly oversimplify the intricate problems of good and evil result in clumsy miscarriages of discipline and in faulty training. We are in need of an ampler knowledge of the mechanisms of mental growth and motivation. This would lead to wiser methods of child care, and a more discerning respect for the individual child.

Growth is governed by principles of relativity. Developmentalism is a philosophic doctrine which acknowledges these principles, and recognizes that the behavior of the child is subject to natural laws of development—laws which are end products of ages of evolution.

The task of the life sciences will be greater than that of the atomic sciences, because the life sciences, under heightened social pressure, will need to define in some measure the very goals of living. Such science will be instrumental, even technological, in its purposefulness. But it will also be humanistic for it would have an aesthetic integrity of its own. It would in itself be a value and a creator of values for the rising generation.

As late as March 1939 there was a Committee for War Prophylaxis working bravely under the banner of the Medical Association of Netherlands. The secretary of this committee made a valiant effort to place "the knowledge and the influence of the medical world at the disposal of peoples and their political leaders." He had already collected 350 titles of books and papers dealing with the psychology of war.

But the war came. And it came with cosmic impact and certitude. Whether a larger and more punctual committee of men of good will could have forestalled the gigantic onslaught must remain a question which should be asked even if there is no answer. For if we do not ask the question, we are already defeated.

Psychiatry, as that branch of medicine which alleviates the sufferings of disintegrated and traumatized minds, will have stupendous tasks for years to come, even when "the war" is past, for the aftermath is longer and worse than the scourge itself. It is now said that the aim of the war is to so reconstruct the world that another apocalypse of violence will not be necessary. How can this be done, except by a profound, socialized reaffirmation of the dignity of life as it is embodied in infancy and childhood? The violence of war outrages the dignities of death. The problem is not to escape death, but to protect the functions of death for the living and those who are born to survive. Christianity has achieved symbolic and ritual solutions of this eternal paradox of life and death. But out of these historic solutions new orientations must be achieved if we are to escape the profanation of technologic violence.

We must bring the science and technology of the race so powerfully to bear upon the protection of developing life that the irreverence of undiscriminating violence will become unthinkable, impossible.

A heightened solicitude for the early years of human growth will not only have a therapeutic benefit for the adult inheritors of the aftermath; it must be the basis for all prophylaxis of war. For how can we ever overcome senseless destruction of life if life and growth are not cherished at their source?

Index

Accelerated behavior, 143
  See also Genius
Acculturation, 83, 93, 94
Adaptive behavior, 184, 191
Age norms, 185, 193
Aldrich, C. Anderson, 71, 75, 79
Amatruda, Catherine S., 186, 190, 204
Amentia, 189-201
  and cerebral palsy, 195-197
  degrees of, 192
  and environmental retardation, 197, 198
  and epilepsy, 203
  and prematurity, 199
  and pseudo-symptomatic retardation, 198
  and sensory deprivation, 200
American Academy of Pediatrics, 167
American Social Science Association, 40, 41
  registers of, 40, 41
Ames, Louise B., 112, 116, 128
Anatomy and the Problem of Behavior, 50
Anthropology, 56
  and documentation of infant behavior, 82-95
Anthroponomy, 82
Apocrypha, 14
Aristotle, 13, 66
Arrangements
  for examination, 186
    illustration of, 31
Association,
  laws of, 66
Atlas of Infant Behavior, 86, 87, 127
Atom, 3

Banker, H. J., 62
Barcroft, J., 118, 119, 125
The Beagle, 149
Behavior
  accelerated, 143
  charting development of, 85
  day, 95
  development of, 85, 187
  diagnosis of, 184
  fields of, 184
  forms, 182
  growth, 182
  infant,
    predictiveness of, 109-116

Behavior—*Continued*
  patterns, 182
  See also Cube behavior
Behaviorism, 71
Bell, Sir Charles, 36, 49
Bernard, Claude, 118, 137, 160
Biological psychology, 45-57
Birth injury. *See* Cerebral palsy
Blake, Henry T., 41
Blakeslee, A. F., 62
Blindness, 174, 201
Block building. *See* Cube building
Body-mind relationship, 5
Boy A, 130, 131, 133, 134
  illustration of, 27
Boy B, 130, 131, 133, 134, 135
Boy D, 130, 131, 133, 134, 135
  illustration of, 27
Bregman, E. C., 76, 79

Campbell, C. MacFie, 73
Carrell, Alexis, 151
Cerebral palsy, 176, 195-197
  devastating injury, 195
  minimal injury, 196
  selective injury, 196
Certification
  by American Board of Pediatrics, 205
Charting
  behavior development, 85
  of mental growth, 101
Chemistry, 50
Chicago
  Exhibit,
    illustration of, 17
  Museum of Science and Industry, 3, 11, 14
  Psychological Museum, 45
Child
  development
    clinical protection of, 187
    science of,
      cultural significance of, 214-217
      scientific study of, 33-106
  preschool
    handicapped, 170-180
    status of, 165-169
Chimerical embryo, 157

INDEX

INDEX

Set in Linotype Baskerville
Format by A. W. Rushmore
Manufactured by The Haddon Craftsmen
Published by HARPER & BROTHERS, *New York*

A

D